Mental Health and the Community:
Problems, Programs, and Strategies

Community Mental Health Series

SHELDON R. ROEN, *Editor*

Research Contributions from Psychology to Community Mental Health
Edited by JERRY W. CARTER, JR.

From Dependency to Dignity: Individual and Social Consequences of a Neighborhood House
LOUIS A. ZURCHER and ALVIN E. GREEN with
EDWARD JOHNSON and SAMUEL PATTON

Coordinate Index Reference Guide to Community Mental Health
STUART E. GOLANN

Mental Health and the Community: Problems, Programs, and Strategies
Edited by MILTON F. SHORE and FORTUNE V. MANNINO

Mental Health and the Community: Problems, Programs, and Strategies

Edited by

MILTON F. SHORE, Ph.D.

and

FORTUNE V. MANNINO, Ph.D.

Mental Health Study Center
National Institute of Mental Health

BEHAVIORAL PUBLICATIONS
NEW YORK, N.Y.

Library of Congress Catalog Card No. 68-59451
The George Bernard Shaw quotation by permission of
The Society of Authors, London, as agent for the Bernard Shaw estate.
Copyright © 1969, except editorial material and Chapter 9,
Behavioral Publications, Inc.
2852 Broadway
New York, N.Y. 10025
Printed in the United States of America

Second Printing, 1971

For Mindel and Verna Rose, whose roles in one small community allowed us to think of larger community problems.

*What made this brain of mine, do you think?
Not the need to move my limbs; for a rat with
half my brain moves as well as I. Not merely
the need to do, but the need to know what I do,
lest in my blind efforts to live I should be
slaying myself.*

—GEORGE BERNARD SHAW

Contents

v

Foreword

Community mental health as a social movement and professional endeavor is a relatively new approach—though its antecedents extend back through the ages. As a formal endeavor, however, the host of mental health programs—such as that establishing the nearly 300 community mental health centers under recent Federal legislation—fall into the Project Head Start category: they are under five years of age. There are, among these programs, a handful of adolescents, and only a select few have reached the 21 years denoting the age of maturity.

The Mental Health Study Center, founded in 1948, falls into this rare last category. The Study Center has been one of the outstanding leaders in community mental health. Its roster of alumni represents a cross-section of the current leadership in the national mental health establishment, as well as at the regional, state, and local levels, among commissioners, program directors, professors, and many others.

The Study Center continues its vigorous leadership role through efforts such as those reflected in this volume. Both Milton F. Shore, a psychologist, and Fortune V. Mannino, a social worker, have taken a creative look at the total view of mental health. They have done it, not from the base of the university nor of a money-giving agency, but of a real-life facility providing mental health services in a local community every day.

Their selections and the total approach of the entire volume reflect the community, the place where problems arise and the place where they must be solved.

I feel that perhaps the most significant aspect of this work is its help in closing the credibility gap between our rich theories and our impoverished services, between our supersalesman rhetoric and the realities of practical experience as utilized by outstanding leaders in achieving program implementation.

The community is as difficult to define and describe as the sea. The variety and dimensions of the community—its sanctions and supports, its needs and resistances—emerge in fresh perspective almost daily. But, through the case-study approach we have here, we can focus on everyday examples. As recounted in this volume, the many tasks—with their similarities and their differences—permit us to recheck not only our theories but our values as well.

This book helps us in feeling both more comfortable and more humble; it also makes us more anxious than ever to try to be as realistic as possible in defining the field of community mental health.

In the area of community help there is a continuum at one end of which is an effusion of humanitarian ideology and the power politics of a social movement and at the other an advanced, sophisticated, psychosocial, ecological theorizing that attempts to explain the phenomenology of man and his environment. In the middle of these two is community mental health, where dedicated lay and professional leaders attempt to practice what they preach.

Their efforts are well documented in this volume, which will make the book of great interest to all those concerned with the mental health of the community and man's propensity to both illness and health.

Between the opening chapter describing efforts to reverse the destructive cycle of poverty in the "psychiatric capital city," Topeka, and its closing utopian description of planning the new city of Columbia outside the nation's capital, this book illustrates the state of the art in the field of community mental health.

One of the aspects of community mental health is social change: the agents of that change will act through the social intervention of the employees of the community mental health center. Earlier articles clearly indicate the difficulties of implementation and operation of community programs as opposed to planning and proposals.

Useful tips for mental health workers are much in evidence throughout the book. Each of the contributions here is a personal one—while discussing major social efforts, such as urban renewal and community mobilization, an author emerges as a practitioner. He molds, melds, and makes things happen. But the articles have a "here is how it happened" unpretentiousness.

Only certain aspects of an author's personality show through the cloak of the written word, however. I found some of the contributions so much more understandable because I knew the men who wrote them. If only we could have books written on video tape!

One theme is clear in all the papers included here. And that is that the scene is much more complex than it seems. Even the approach to a problem such as providing mental health services to a school system—knowing how diverse and varied school systems are—is more complicated than one's original expectations.

This complexity is shown in the brave attempt by the editors to divide the book into three main categories, social action, clinical approaches, and problem solving. Many of the articles cover more than one division, but the attempt, in the main, is successful.

My feeling is that Shore and Mannino have made an excellent contribution to community mental health. Whether or not the reader agrees with me will be decided eleven chapters from this point.

BERTRAM S. BROWN, M.D.
Deputy Director
National Institute of Mental Health
Chevy Chase, Maryland
June, 1968

Preface

The idea for a book that described in detail a variety of community mental health programs was germinated in discussions with many colleagues at the National Institute of Mental Health, particularly those at the Mental Health Study Center, an NIMH community research and service unit in Prince George's County, Maryland. The idea came to fruition through the support of Dr. Sheldon Roen, editor of the *Community Mental Health Journal*. All agreed that community mental health had reached the stage where theories and ideas were being rapidly translated into action programs of many kinds. However, they all felt that as yet few reports of how programs were initiated and implemented were available. Those that could be found were frequently not easily accessible, nor did they cover the range of activities encompassed by those involved in the field.

We are grateful to our colleagues at the Institute, especially Dr. Samuel Buker, Dr. Quentin Rae-Grant, Dr. James W. Osberg, Dr. Bertram S. Brown, and Dr. Stanley F. Yolles, who encouraged us to proceed. Mr. Herbert L. Rooney deserves special thanks for critically reviewing the manuscript. Miss Charlotte Malasky helped with the details of putting the book into final form. Mrs. Marcia Ridgely typed and re-typed the manuscripts until they were almost memorized. Mrs. Julia Reed and Mrs. Shirley Robinson carefully proofread the work. We thank them all.

Above all, we are grateful to the contributors who agreed to share some of their personal experiences and graciously bore the pressures of meeting deadlines.

We would like to make clear that the views expressed in this book are those of the editors and the contributors, and official endorsement by the National Institute of Mental Health, the Public Health Service, or the Department of Health, Education, and Welfare should neither be inferred nor suggested. The opinions expressed herein do not necessarily represent the official policies of those agencies. The National Institute of Mental Health felt this book might be a contribution toward the understanding of issues related to national concerns in the area of mental health. The contributors were selected as representatives of certain trends in the community mental health field. Their programs should in no way be taken as exhaustive of the variety of activities and opinions in the area.

Responsibility for any errors in judgment or taste other than in the individual articles rests solely with the editors.

Contributors

SEYMOUR R. KAPLAN, M.D.
Assistant Professor of Psychiatry
Associate Director, Mental Health Services
Lincoln Hospital
Albert Einstein College of Medicine
New York, N.Y.

WILLIAM H. KEY, PH.D.
Chairman, Department of Sociology
University of Denver
University Park
Denver, Colorado

FRANK KIESLER, M.D.
Program Director
Northland Area Mental Health Program
Grand Rapids, Minnesota;
Clinical Associate Professor of Psychiatry
University of Minnesota Medical School
Minneapolis, Minnesota

PAUL V. LEMKAU, M.D.
Professor of Mental Hygiene
School of Hygiene and Public Health
The Johns Hopkins University
Baltimore, Maryland

BERYCE W. MACLENNAN, PH.D.
Chief, Consultation and Community Liaison Section
Mental Health Study Center
National Institute of Mental Health
Adelphi, Maryland;
formerly, Associate Director in Charge of Training
Institute for Youth Studies
Howard University
Washington, D.C.

JOSEPH L. MASSIMO, ED.D.
Chief Psychologist
Newton Public Schools
Newton, Massachusetts;
Assistant Clinical Professor of Psychiatry
Boston University School of Medicine
Boston, Massachusetts

CONTRIBUTORS

HARRIS B. PECK, M.D.
Associate Professor of Psychiatry
Director, Mental Health Services
Lincoln Hospital
Albert Einstein College of Medicine
New York, N.Y.

QUENTIN RAE-GRANT, M.D.
Director, Mental Health Study Center
National Institute of Mental Health
Adelphi, Maryland;
formerly, Director, Mental Health Division
St. Louis County Health Department
St. Louis, Missouri

DWIGHT W. RIEMAN, M.S.S.A.
Administrative Consultant
Texas Department of Mental Health
and Mental Retardation
Austin, Texas

MILTON F. SHORE, PH.D.
Chief, Clinical Research and Program
Evaluation Section
Mental Health Study Center
National Institute of Mental Health
Adelphi, Maryland;
formerly, Chief Psychologist
Newton-Baker Project
Newton, Massachusetts

LORENE A. STRINGER, M.S.W.
Community Mental Health Coordinator
St. Louis County Health Department
St. Louis, Missouri

HAROLD H. WEISSMAN, D.S.W.
Assistant Executive Director for
Research and Development
Mobilization for Youth
New York, N.Y.

H.G. WHITTINGTON, M.D.
Director of Psychiatry
Denver Department of Health and Hospitals
Denver, Colorado

LOUIS A. ZURCHER, PH.D
Department of Sociology
University of Texas
Austin, Texas

Introduction

Community mental health[1] is generally recognized as one of the most significant movements of health care in recent years. Not only have community mental health ideas had an effect on the priority, distribution, and delivery of mental health services, but they have also had a significant impact on the community service structure. In addition, they have stimulated great interest in the relevance to mental health of such pressing social issues as poverty and unemployment (as well as the reverse—the relevance of mental health principles to social issues). However, the rapid growth of mental health programs and the expansion of concern to broader and more socially based problems has been accompanied by a whole new set of problems for the mental health practitioner-administrator. As Peck points out in his chapter in this volume, "No adequate theoretical framework, overall strategy, or system of techniques (has been) generally available . . ." for the implementation of the principles underlying the community mental health concept. In other words, many community-based mental health programs are being organized for which there is little precedent in the background and experiences of the mental health professionals.

This lack of precedent is a double-edged sword. Although often resulting in frustration, anxiety, and sometimes even failure, it also offers opportunities for the development and experimental testing of new ideas, some based on traditional models, others breaking new ground. The result, since the advent of the Federal Centers legislation in 1963 (as well as legislation in the areas of education, poverty, and welfare, which have incorporated mental health dimensions), has been the active involvement of many psychiatrists, psychologists, social workers, sociologists, community planners, indigenous workers, and volunteers in a variety of new roles, activities, and programs. Out of this involvement have arisen certain experiences related to implementing community mental health programs that are of general interest. It has been only recently that these programs have developed far enough so that one is able to get an overview of the goals, the specific problems in implementation, and some notion of the significance of the program within the total context of the community mental health movement.

The purpose of this book is to begin to fill in the gaps between theoretical ideas on community mental health and program planning and implementation.

[1]For this volume "community mental health" can be defined as that area that assumes that mental health and mental illness cannot be understood adequately unless there is a focus on the interrelationship between the individual and his social context and that programs are set up based on this premise.

xiii

It attempts to present the diverse ways in which programs are implemented in various areas by people of different disciplines. Each chapter is an original contribution by a person actively involved in the struggles of translating community mental health ideas into specific action programs. In writing about their programs, each contributor was asked to organize his material around the following outline:

1. Initiation of the program. What were the program objectives? How was the mandate obtained and what were the community problems to which it was related? How was the project conceived and initiated?

2. Implementation. Who was contacted? What were the methods used, that is, was the program imposed on or generated by the community?

3. How was community support gained and maintained?What feedback was there?

4. How were resistances handled or overcome?

5. What does the program indicate with regard to what needs to be known about the community in which the program will be carried out? What are the implications for the mental health profession?

The contributors, because of limited space, were asked not to describe the details of their programs (most of the programs have been described in other publications), nor to focus on any effort that was being made to evaluate program effectiveness. In reality, however, each contributor used the outline described not only to discuss problems of implementation but also to conclude, generalize, conceptualize, and make recommendations on the basis of his experiences. Thus, in a way this book can be seen as a series of essays generated from detailed case studies of community mental health programs. It is hoped that in this way the experiences of a few may be made relevant to the many professionals dealing with similar problems, tasks, and issues.

The book is divided into four sections:

I. *Programs with a social action orientation*

These programs attempt to deal with general community problems, such as poverty and housing, and are oriented toward change of certain aspects of the social structure of the community.

II. *Programs with a mental health service orientation*

These programs, rather than dealing with general community problems related to mental health, focus on the expansion and coordination of mental health services. This may take the form of reorganization and redistribution of mental health services, or it may result in innovative directions, such as new uses or sources of manpower or new ways of service delivery.

III. *Programs with a problem-solving orientation*

These programs were generated by the need to resolve specific social or personal problems. They aim, for example, to identify high-risk groups in certain areas. Although the program may expand in many directions, its effectiveness lies primarily in the reduction of identified symptom groups, such as delinquent behavior.

IV. *Programs that open new areas*

Community mental health has led to the use of mental health professionals in new ways. These include consultants, administrators, and community planners. Issues that arise in these new roles often pose very specific problems, some of which are presented in this section.

Although there is a great deal of overlap in the sections (New Careers, for example, was in great part generated by efforts to deal with problems in delinquency, and mental health service programs have many elements of social action), we feel that such a division is helpful in differentiating the knowledge needed before intervening, the level of the intervention, the techniques used, and the way resistances are handled. But above all, these different approaches are each based on certain values and assumptions. It is these values and assumptions that together form the total fabric of this volume, a fabric that the editors will attempt to weave together through their commentary on the sections and on each chapter.

Part I

Programs with a Social Action Orientation

One of the major assumptions in community mental health is that mental health problems are a function of both the individual and his relevant socio-cultural environment. The traditional patient-oriented approach focused chiefly upon the individual and his psychological dysfunctions. Greater emphasis has been placed recently upon those social forces that generate, foster, and/or perpetuate disordered behavior in the person.

Although much remains to be learned about the interactions between psychological needs and social factors, a large body of data has already been accumulated. Sociologists and social psychologists have, for instance, related personality variables, such as adaptational styles and self-image, to social and cultural variables, such as socioeconomic level, racial segregation, migration, and disorganized community structures. But, despite this knowledge, it has only been recently that these professions have been actively involved in the problems of implementing their theoretical formulations by attempting to bring about planned change in constructive mental health directions. (Prior to their involvement, such implementation was primarily the responsibility of social workers trained in community organization.)

The sociological perspective has been most valuable in identifying those relevant social organizations that must be mobilized and worked with if any social changes are to occur. Implicit in sociological theory is the assumption that significant changes in large numbers of individuals cannot occur unless there are changes in the organizational structures that make up the individual's social field. How such structures were utilized in bringing about a community action program developed to break the destructive cycle of poverty is described in one article in this section. A second article deals with an urban renewal program organized to avoid the personal problems arising from forced relocation. A third article in this section, written by a social worker trained in community organization, describes how a community was helped to evaluate its mental health needs, to plan for services, and to initiate specific programs.

Chapter 1
Implementing a Community Action Agency
Louis A. Zurcher

There is little doubt that if one were to identify the groups of highest risk from a mental health point of view, one would unhesitatingly have to include those who, in an affluent society, are experiencing the severe deprivations resulting from living in poverty. Throughout the years there have been many attempts to break the cycle of poverty. The most recent of these attempts was the passage of the Economic Opportunity Act of 1964, which established the Office of Economic Opportunity (OEO) as an agency directly responsible to the President of the United States. The elements of this act that were new lay not in the dispensing of Federal funds, but in the attempts to intervene to break some of the cultural aspects of poverty that have tended to perpetuate deprivation from generation to generation. These efforts led to the formulation of new programs based on the community action concept. Community action characteristically refers to action that emerges from the community and that involves local individuals and organizations in new patterns of interaction aimed toward the planning and implementing of programs that will produce changes in the social climate, geared toward resolving such destructive community problems as the poverty cycle.[1] Often such changes occur only after bitter struggles among community forces. How a community action program was implemented rather smoothly by social science understanding of the forces operating at a given time is described by Dr. Zurcher.

[1]Warren, R. L. *The Community in America.* Chicago: Rand McNally and Company, 1963.

6

Chapter 1

Implementing a Community Action Agency

Louis A. Zurcher

The Economic Opportunity Act of 1964 established the Office of Economic Opportunity (OEO) and released Federal funds for a "war" to be waged against poverty. The most innovative and subsequently most controversial provision of the Act (under Title II) made it possible for qualifying applicant communities to create locally based and operated "community action agencies." Each community action agency (CAA) was to be responsible for acquiring, implementing, and coordinating additional poverty programming, but *must* do so with "maximum feasible participation" of the poor.

The rationale for "maximum feasible participation" of the poor (later defined by OEO to mean that at least one-third of the membership of all policy-making poverty boards, councils, and committees must be elected or democratically appointed representatives of the poor) clearly revealed a social therapy strategy for poverty amelioration. Traditional welfare practices and services generally had been assessed to encourage psychological dependency among the poor and consequently to perpetuate rather than disrupt the generational cycle of poverty (Ferman, Kornbluh, & Haber, 1965; Gans, 1964; Haggstrom, 1964). On the other hand, evidence had been accumulating that demonstrated beneficial impact upon the self-esteem and seeking motivations of low-income persons who had meaningfully participated in social action (Brager, 1964; Fishman & Solomon, 1963; Wittenberg, 1948). Reflecting those assessments and findings, the CAA's by design were expected not only to administer services *to* and develop programs *for* the poor, but to provide them significant participation in decision-making and administrative processes relevant to the services and programs. By their participation the poor were to evolve a greater sense of control over their environment, more self-confidence, and were to feel less powerless in, alienated from, and dependent upon the community at large. The poor were to have the opportunity to learn new social roles and skills, thereby increasing their alternatives for adaptation and change and liberating some of the restrictions upon the self-determined use of their own potentials.

There are often striking differences between the intent and the implementation of social legislation. That should not be surprising, since social legislation is sifted through already long-established and change-resisting community political and social organization. In many American communities CAA's become foci for bitter struggles—primarily because "maximum feasible representation," if realized, could mean a small but nonetheless sudden shift (toward the poor) in the distribution of community power and influence and would challenge accustomed though arbitrary socioeconomic and ethnic barriers.

At this writing, 1,100 CAA's funded by OEO are operating in the United States. CAA's differ from one another insofar as the communities of which they are part differ demographically, politically, and socially. Furthermore, CAA's vary in the manner in which they were initiated and implemented within the community—by whom and for whom. However, all have in common OEO funding, programming and jurisdiction, and the mandates of the Economic Opportunity Act.

This chapter will discuss some dynamics and dilemmas observed during the initiation and implementation of one CAA (The Topeka Office of Economic Opportunity) in one community (Topeka, Kansas). Though the data are derived from study of a single case and generalizations can only cautiously be made, analysis of the formative processes and staff experience of the Topeka Office of Economic Opportunity may yield useful information for those practitioners who would be social interveners.

The Community and Initiation of the CAA

Topeka, the capital of Kansas, has a population of approximately 125,000 (8% Negro, 3.5% Mexican-American, 0.8% American Indian). Less than 2% of the citizens are unemployed, and less than 1% are the recipients of welfare. The median annual income for the Topeka family is $6,000, with 15.5% of families earning less than $3,000 per year. There are no crowded tenements, no shantytowns, no organized protest, nor any of the other more dramatic and headline-making evidences of chronic poverty.

A comparative neighborhood-by-neighborhood analysis of socioeconomic conditions in Topeka yields, however, a more revealing set of statistics. Some of the neighborhoods have 10% of the people unemployed, 20% on welfare, and 30% of the housing substandard (Topeka-Shawnee Regional Planning Commission, 1965). Perhaps typical of many other rural and small urban communities in the Midwest, Topeka sustains quiet, relatively unseen poverty pockets.

Late in 1964 the Topeka Welfare Planning Council became interested in the programs available through the newly formed Office of Economic Opportunity. The council, a volunteer citizens' group of approximately 200 community leaders, professionals, and businessmen, had with support from the United Fund demonstrated prior interest in Topeka's social problems. A council subcommittee was formed to investigate the possibility of establishing a CAA in Topeka and consisted of nine members—two city commissioners, the executive director of the United Fund, the director of the Topeka Human Relations Commission, the city director of recreation, the superintendent of schools, the president of the council, a research associate at the Menninger Foundation, and the head of the Department of Sociology at Washburn University (chairman of the subcommittee).

After considerable deliberation, the subcommittee decided to apply for a one-year OEO planning and development grant, and received commitment from the Topeka Welfare Planning Council for the mandatory 10% "local share" of total program funding. The first phase of the planning period was to be used to structure and staff a skeleton CAA and to develop an organizational rationale and strategy for poverty amelioration that would be *community-wide* in scope. The next phase was to involve an assessment of community needs and presently available resources to meet those needs. The third phase would focus upon ways and means of enlisting participation from among both the poor and not-poor and of gaining cooperation and support from already existing community agencies. The final phase would include the organizational solidifying and expansion of the CAA and the acquisition of additional OEO funded programming as needed.

Since the poor were only indirectly represented in the Topeka Welfare Planning Council, the subcommittee chose the planning and development grant alternative to provide time for the evolution of a CAA that would maximize opportunity for significant participation of the poor. It would have been possible for the council immediately to be awarded large amounts of poverty money, which they then could have administered with only token representation from among the poor. However, they chose to start slowly, attempting a community-wide effort toward implementing the mandate of the Economic Opportunity Act (for further discussion of the initiation of the CAA, see: Topeka OEO, 1966, pp. 1–10).

On May 1, 1965, OEO awarded the planning and development grant to the Topeka Welfare Planning Council. The council formally inaugurated the CAA with the name "Topeka Office of Economic Opportunity" (Topeka OEO), leased office space in one of the low-income neighborhoods, and hired a director (white Methodist minister, three times elected from a poverty area to the Kansas State Legislature, former research associate at the Menninger Foundation and council subcommittee member) and an assistant director (Mexican-American working man, 15 years' experience as a union and civil rights organizer and official). Together with the subcommittee members, the new Topeka OEO staff began to plan the community's "war against poverty."

Method of Study

The author began the study of the Topeka OEO in September, 1965 (later with grant support from the Office of Economic Opportunity). Significant events concerning the formation of the CAA prior to that time were reconstructed from interviews with the Topeka OEO staff and participants, with members of the Topeka Welfare Planning Council, and by analysis of the CAA applications, records, and reports. To avoid interfering with the development of the Topeka OEO and to minimize threat to beginning participants, the research methods primarily employed were the field techniques of participant observation and unstructured interviews. Parallel observers were used wherever and whenever possible in order to heighten reliability of the data; no observer entered a meeting group unless he could be introduced by someone known and trusted among the group members.

When the data-collecting was terminated in May, 1967, over 200 meetings of various Topeka OEO committees had been attended and documented by a research staff of nine. Approximately 400 unstructured interviews had been conducted with participants. Since the research field station was in the same set of buildings as the Topeka OEO, daily contact had been maintained with the Topeka OEO staff.

Implementation of the CAA

The Topeka OEO staff, supported by the Topeka Welfare Planning Council subcommittee, developed a complex of committees as a strategy for encouraging community participation. The first of these, considered to be temporary and called the City-wide Committee, was composed of the Topeka OEO staff, the subcommittee, and about 20 representatives from the community at large. Through the City-wide Committee the Topeka OEO established a set of 11 Study Committees, each to deal with a specific topic area (e.g., housing, education, employment, etc.), to have its own officers, and to have a membership of topic specialists and representatives from low-income areas. The Study Committees were to assess community needs and resources and to make suggestions toward future proverty programming.

Concerned that the poor still did not have enough opportunity for participation, the Topeka OEO staff, through the City-wide Committee, developed a set of Target Neighborhood Committees. Twelve "Target Neighborhoods" had been designated by the Topeka OEO staff as manifesting high indices of poverty and blight. Each of these was to have a committee of residents, with elected officers, to serve as a forum for neighborhood needs and problems.

Next, it was determined that the City-wide Committee would be restructured as "The Economic Opportunity Board of Shawnee County, Kansas, Incorporated." The board would be composed of no more than 75 voting members—the chairman and vice-chairman of Target Neighborhood Committees, the chairman of Study Committees, and representatives from local government, agencies, businesses, religious, civic, and civil rights groups. As structured, the board would have at least one-third elected representation from among the poor (Target Neighborhood Committee officers) and would be empowered with final approval on all poverty-program budgetary, personnel, and programming matters. As soon as the board was legally incorporated, the Topeka OEO staff were to become its employees; and the Topeka Welfare Council was to terminate its role as a steering body.

The Topeka OEO staff and advisers intended the committee complex not only to generate community action proposals but to foster social therapy among the participants and those whom they would influence. The planners assumed that the opportunity for equal-status interaction among representatives of the poor and not-poor, in structured social situations (the committees) and toward mutually determined goals, would break down stereotypes, open lines of communication, and engender social change. The low-income community would benefit from the funding of various poverty programs, but equally important many of the poor hopefully would be able to enact new and self-enhancing social roles, e.g., voter, elector, proponent or opponent of ideas for neighborhood action, member of a Target Neighborhood Committee, formal or informal committee leader, spokesman and representative on the board, consultant in Study Committees, etc.[1]

In order to serve effectively as a "bridge" the Topeka OEO was intended by the planners to maintain a "middle ground" between the poor and not-poor in the community (Topeka OEO, 1966, p. 10). From that organizationally marginal position, the Topeka OEO staff were to bring poor and not-poor together in joint endeavor toward the amelioration of poverty.[2]

First Committee Meetings

At early meetings of the City-wide Committee the not-poor were overrepresented and the poor were underrepresented. The topics of discussion, dealing primarily with organizational structure, by-laws, etc., were clearly dominated by the not-poor. The meetings ran smoothly, followed parliamentary procedure, and were led by middle-class professionals.

Paralleling the City-wide Committee, the early Study Committee meetings were dominated in numbers and participation by the more verbal and experienced not-poor. Furthermore, the first Target Neighborhood Committee meetings, difficult to organize, showed a general pattern of passiveness among the low-income members.

The Topeka OEO staff were not surprised by these phenomena. They anticipated that the not-poor participants, particularly organizational officials to whom meetings were a way of life, would at the beginning tend to "run the

[1]For a theoretical conceptualization of this model for social change, see Zurcher & Key, 1967.
[2]For a theoretical conceptualization of this organizational position, see Zurcher, 1967a.

show." They also anticipated that the participating poor, involved in such activities perhaps for the first time in their lives, would be unsure of themselves, withdrawn, and generally unconvinced of the worth of committee participation.

The challenge, therefore, was not just to mobilize an organizational structure that would efficiently process new program applications—the experienced not-poor could easily have taken care of that. Rather, the challenge was to provide, within the developing organizational structure and under OEO pressure to produce proposals quickly, the time and room for the participating poor to develop and test new roles.

The Topeka OEO staff met the challenge in two ways. First, the Topeka OEO assistant director was commissioned to concentrate upon organizing the Target Neighborhood Committees. His informal and "regular guy" approach and the fact that he was a native of and lifetime resident in the Target Neighborhood earned him the trust of many neighborhood residents (Zurcher, 1967a, 1967b). He sought latent indigenous leadership among the poor, rallied his friends and acquaintances, and talking "their language," convinced several residents that organizing a Neighborhood Committee of their *own* would help them to "get in on the action." By October, 1965 (when the Economic Opportunity Board was incorporated), 10 Target Neighborhood Committees had been established and were sending their officers as representatives to other committee meetings.

The neighborhood residents felt a sense of ownership for their Neighborhood Committees. Since all the members were neighborhood residents and almost always were poor, the individual participant was less hesitant to speak up, to "try on" a new role. A sense of "we" grew, which engendered new competencies in many of the participants, but in particular in the elected officers, who had to represent the neighborhood in interaction with "them" (not-poor). The experiences in the Neighborhood Committees generalized to participation in other committees more representative of the community at large.

As a second attempt to maintain an organizational structure open to the growing skills of the participating poor, the staff steadfastly refused to let the Topeka OEO become a "proposal mill." Rather, they insisted that ideas for community action originate in the Neighborhood Committees (at times stimulated by the staff or Study Committees). Then the ideas were to evolve through phases of grant preparation, budget analysis, and Economic Opportunity Board approval, with periodic review by the originating neighborhood(s). The procedure was slow, "inefficient" by bureaucratic standards, but did allow greater participation of the poor in decision-making than a more "streamlined" procedure might have.

At the end of seven months' operation, the Topeka OEO had forwarded to Washington only two OEO community action proposals (for a day-care center and an extension-worker program). Both proposals had, however, slowly coursed through the entire committee complex and provided process experience for no fewer than 500 participants, most of them poor.

A Pioneer Proposal

The major difficulties encountered by the CAA during its implementation are revealed by tracing, in some detail, the evolution of one of the first community action proposals.

In accordance with the Topeka OEO's design that community action proposals should originate among the poor, two Target Neighborhood Committees jointly determined that they needed indigenous nonprofessionals who could serve as liaison between neighborhood residents and existing agencies and organizations.[1] The neighborhood officers felt that one of the enduring problems of poverty was the perpetuated inability of the poor actively to use community resources for neighborhood and self-improvement. The Neighborhood Committee members discussed their ideas in several of the Study Committees and with OEO and agency officials. The local Recreation Commission showed interest in sponsoring "extension workers," who would be hired from among the poor and would serve as "troubleshooters" and "go-betweens" in the Target Neighborhoods. After further discussion the Recreation Commission agreed to be the program's "delegate agency" and provided the community's share of funding. With board and Target Neighborhood Committee approval, the Topeka OEO submitted a formal OEO community action proposal to Washington in August, 1965.

The Neighborhood Committee members had during late summer, 1965, ardently gathered supporting surveys and documents for the proposal, and had taken copies of their proposal draft to several city officials and community leaders. The interaction among these representatives from disparate socioeconomic groups was most encouraging to the CAA planners—stereotypes seemed to be eroding. Most importantly, the neighborhood participants were becoming enthusiastic about the potential of OEO and their own participation in community affairs. They felt a sense of ownership of and pride in the proposal.

However, months elapsed while the extension worker proposal was under review by regional and national OEO. During the interim, several substantial changes were made in the proposal, some at the request of the Federal grant reviewers, some generated by the local delegate agency's further defining the place of the program in its organizational policies and procedures. The neighborhood participants were not happy with the delay, nor with the modifications, both of which were perceived to have been "decided in high places" and "not by us." The lack of reinforcement for their participation began to take its toll, and attendance at the sponsoring Target Neighborhood Committees meet-

[1]Indigenous nonprofessional programs are discussed in detail by Reiff and Riessman, 1965.

ings began to fall off. One of the neighborhood chairmen canceled several meetings because he feared "the members would ask about the proposal, and I had no answers for them." Over time, the sense of program pride and ownership diminished among the neighborhood participants. "*Our* proposal" as a referent faded into "*that* proposal." When finally, in late December, 1965, the proposal was approved and implemented by the delegate agency, "*that* proposal" had faded to "*their* proposal" and open acknowledgement of the delegate agency's ownership.[4]

The Topeka OEO's announcement that the extension worker proposal had been approved brought little enthusiasm from the members of the two sponsoring Target Neighborhood Committees. The Recreation Commission, quite in keeping with their understanding of the functions of a delegate agency, intended to determine job descriptions, hire the program personnel, and to administer the program in coordination with their superordinate organizational goals. The neighborhood participants, on the other hand, thought they were to have more say in the determination of the program basics and in the actual program implementation. As a result, there followed a number of clashes at the Economic Opportunity Board meetings between Recreation Commission staff and Target Neighborhood officers, clashes centering around definitions of power and control and generally resolved by divided vote of the Board in favor of the delegate agency.

The CAA in the Middle

The Topeka OEO was caught in the middle of the conflicting expectations concerning the extension worker program. The Recreation Commission understandably interpreted its "delegate agency" function as program responsibility, broadly considered, and felt that administrative prerogatives had clearly been delegated to them contractually by the Economic Opportunity Board and the Topeka OEO staff. The Target Neighborhood participants interpreted their "maximum feasible participation" to include some of the program responsibilities and administrative tasks they saw had become the property of the Recreation Commission. A considerable amount of the confusion in expectations stemmed from the vagueness of the terms "delegate agency" and "maximum feasible participation"—terms which the Topeka OEO, still in its infancy, had been unable to clearly define. Thus, working definitions painfully had to evolve during the processing of the pioneer proposal. The working definitions, occasionally clarified or complicated by regional and/or national OEO, were never quite so simple or universally understood as might have been anticipated by CAA planners.

[4]The involvement of neighborhood participants in the extension worker proposal is further discussed by Zurcher, Green, Johnson, & Patton, 1969.

The Topeka OEO staff found themselves in the uncomfortable position of trying to reconcile neighborhood participants' demands for "action now" and immediate results for their proposal with the delays of OEO proposal review and the "careful, long-range planning" of the delegate agency. Furthermore, the Topeka OEO staff were faced with the dilemma of how to distribute program power in a situation where both program and power were differentially interpreted and at the same time changing through development. At times when expectations conflicted, the staff were tempted to abandon the Topeka OEO's designed marginal position and identify exclusively either with the poor or the not-poor (with greater pressures and potential rewards for the latter). Though alignment with one or the other segment of the community would have made their task easier, or at least more identifiable, the staff chose to remain committed to the "bridge" rationale, acknowledging that they would never be able to satisfy all of the diverse expectations of the participants in the poverty program. Subsequently, the staff adopted a working philosophy functional for accommodating the personal stresses they would encounter amid the conflicting or unfulfilled expectations. They postulated that "social change makes waves" and "the chemistry of bringing the poor and not-poor together can be explosive." They defined themselves as "agents for the social change" and accepted the "flak" as part of the job.

A Solution from the Neighborhood

Though the extension worker program was effectively being mobilized by the delegate agency and workers were being hired from among the poor, members of the two Target Neighborhood Committees that had originally sponsored the proposal continued to be disappointed with their "loss of the program." The Topeka OEO staff, though satisfied with the way the delegate agency was handling the extension worker program, realized that the issue of control was frustrating neighborhood participants. The staff further realized that though the preparation of the pioneer proposal had manifested "maximum feasible participation" of the poor, the implementation of the funded program had not. Therefore, both the neighborhood participants and the Topeka OEO staff sought innovations for further proposals that would result in more program control for the poor.

Members of one of the two Target Neighborhood Committees that had sponsored the extension worker program decided they wanted to develop a "neighborhood house" in their area. A neighborhood house would be on their own "turf," and thus their ownership would be less mercurial.

The Topeka OEO staff was enthusiastic about the program possibilities, and together with the neighborhood participants summarized the formal goals of such a house: (1) to provide a point of contact between low-income persons and existing services and to provide bridges between the persons and the services; (2) to provide a rallying point and a home base for the people in the neighborhood for the promotion of OEO and other related groups; (3) to provide a full range of counseling services for all age groups of the neighborhood; (4) to provide a place for family education on food marketing and preparation, clothing, consumer education, and any other courses that would help to strengthen family life; (5) to provide a place for part-time care of preschool children; (6) to provide an outlet for leisure time activities for the people of the neighborhood; and (7) to provide a place for the training of professionals and nonprofessionals in how to work with people in a low-income neighborhood (Topeka, OEO, 1966, pp. 16–17). For the Target Neighborhood participants, the informal goals of the house were equally clear— "to run our own program."

The officers and members of the Target Neighborhood Committee chose their own source of local share funding and picked their own advisory council from the community at large. They guided the proposal through its development and though depending upon Topeka OEO staff for coordination and advice, clearly cast them in the peripheral role of consultants. In April, 1966, the house proposal was submitted to regional OEO; and two months later it was approved. During the two-month review, the chairman of the sponsoring Neighborhood Committee carefully and personally followed the proposal's progress and reported every detail to his constituency. The Topeka OEO staff similarly sought review information from the regional OEO and shared it with the Neighborhood Committee.

As soon as the house was funded, the neighborhood participants, with the requested help of the Topeka OEO staff and the advisory council, vigorously and tenaciously began implementing the program. They wrote job descriptions and hired personnel (all from the neighborhood in which the house was to function), selected the building, purchased fixtures and supplies, etc. Some conflicts were generated between the Topeka OEO staff and the neighborhood house leaders when the former had to exert supervisory prerogatives as the coordinating CAA and the latter pressed for continuing autonomy. Those conflicts became fewer and less severe as role boundaries, administrative tasks, and areas of mutual support became clearer to both CAA and house principals. [5]

That the Topeka OEO staff had remained committed to their "bridge" position between the poor and not-poor seemed to contribute to the climate that made it possible for neighborhood participants *actively* to turn disappointment with the extension worker proposal into satisfaction with the neighborhood house. Furthermore, the bridge position gave the CAA access to community agencies and organizations, and thus it was able to help the neighborhood house acquire local share from a nonrestricting delegate agency.

[5]For a detailed case history of the evolution of the neighborhood house, see Zurcher, Green, Johnson, and Patton, 1969.

Though some role boundaries had to be defined by direct confrontation between the Topeka OEO and neighborhood house leaders, the CAA had to this point remained flexible and open enough to provide support to neighborhood participants when needed and yet to accommodate the increasing needs of neighborhood participants for autonomy and self-direction. This flexibility was maintained despite pressure from Recreation Commission staff, who felt the neighborhood house was a "duplication" of the extension worker services and an indication of CAA administrative errors.

Conclusions

As indicated in this discussion of a few of the experiences of the Topeka OEO, planning a CAA is less complicated than implementing it, once planned. Implementation is uniquely difficult if the CAA is intended to establish and maintain a "bridge" position for the purpose of bringing poor and not-poor together toward the amelioration of poverty.

The CAA intervenes in the status quo of the community, and while declaring and subsequently striving to reach its social goals, can generate diverse expectations, resistances, anxieties, and dissatisfactions among various community components. When it attempts to obey the "maximum feasible participation" mandate of the Economic Opportunity Act, the CAA promulgates social therapy for low-income participants and, if successful, will be challenged to accommodate the participants' expression and testing of autonomy, desire for increasing responsibility and more complex roles, and urge for wider program ownership and control. At the same time, if the local poverty program is intended to be a community-wide endeavor or if financial support is needed, the CAA may have to enlist the cooperation of already established agencies and organizations, without allowing their fixed operating procedures to restrict the potential innovations of the poverty program.

Though the experience of recurring conflict may encourage defensive rigidity, the CAA itself cannot become inflexible in organizational structure or operating procedures if it is to maintain the "bridge" strategy of social intervention. The staff of the CAA that accomplishes social change will, if they have not resigned because of stress, have to evolve a philosophical view of themselves as change agents, and be encouraged by their commitment to a worthwhile task that, ironically, is most stressful when best done.

A Note on Social Intervention and Community Mental Health Centers

Planned social intervention inevitably is concerned with the mental health of the intended beneficiaries. This is particularly apparent in the case of a poverty intervention organization such as the Topeka OEO, whose purposes and goals include social therapy for the participants. Disruption of stereotypes, freedom for interpersonal interaction, mastery over the environment, development and utilization of individual potentials, a greater repertoire of nonrestricting social roles, process experiences yielding self-confidence and self-esteem—all hoped for by-products of participation in the poverty program—are indeed relevant to mental health.

There appear to be some similarities between the CAA and mental health centers opting to serve the low-income areas of a community. Reiff and Riessman (1965) have shown that community *action* can be an essential corollary of a mental health movement. Beiser (1965), Cumming and Cumming (1963), Haggstrom (1964), Leighton (1965), Piven (1966), and Wittenberg (1948) have demonstrated the relationship between social action toward neighborhood or community integration and individual mental health.

If the mental health center in a low-income area is to have a beneficial impact upon the mental health of residents, it appears it would have no choice but to become involved directly or indirectly in social action programs that might ameliorate the physical and (if the poor meaningfully participate) the psychological constrictions of poverty (Riessman, 1965; Riessman & Hallowitz, 1967). In such case, the mental health center would be a social intervener; and its staff agents for social change. The therapeutic strategies and professional roles emerging from that stance, being less in the traditional mode of psychiatric treatment, would have a better chance of being successful with the poor, particularly when indigenous nonprofessionals are extensively involved (Reiff & Riessman, 1965). But commitment to social action can bring upon activists the reverberations of social change, and community pressures both to intensify and to cease their intervention efforts. Mental health professionals, therefore, might find themselves facing an unfamiliar kind of occupational stress. A training program for mental health center employees should include discussion of the dynamics of planned social intervention and social change, and of possible resident responses to the employee's role as change agent. This presupposes, of course, a detailed understanding of the community to be served and the values, expectations, and desires of the residents.

It is probable that community mental health centers will be implemented in low-income areas where, through earlier social intervention programming, participation of the poor has had precedents, or at least been publicized. Involvement of the poor, particularly indigenous leaders among the poor, in the planning and implementation of the center is in those instances more than social therapy—it is a political reality, a sine qua non for the acceptance and effectiveness of the center.

Several of the Topeka Target Neighborhood Committee officers, during one of the last of a year-long series of closed "Research Committee" meetings with the author, shared their views about psychiatry, mental health, and mental health centers. The officers spoke of the frightening "formality" of psychiatrists and anxieties about being "controlled" by them when in treatment. They discussed the "shame" associated with being mentally ill and how terrible it was for courts "to take someone who is sick in the head away from his family." They argued whether or not mental illness was "sickness of the spirit," "a lack of will-power," or "just in the cards." They speculated about the feelings of discomfort and communication difficulties experienced by Negro patients who had white therapists, and "poor" patients who had "rich" therapists. After further ventilation of these somewhat typical attitudes, the officers shifted discussion to "what can be done to get psychiatric help to the poor in a way that they can use it." All of the officers were excited about the potential of the indigenous nonprofessional program for "closing the gap between psychiatrists and the poor." They were also sanguine concerning community mental health centers, but only if they were not "dropped into our neighborhoods like apples off a high branch." The officers felt mental health centers would have to become "part of the neighborhood" to be effective, but could not do so unless "asked by the people." "We've been guinea pigs in life for too long," argued one officer. "Decisions were always made by someone else, supposedly for our own good. Now we've been making a few decisions of our own under OEO. I think mental health centers can be a help to us, but I'd want to be around for the planning of any one in our neighborhood, so nothing would be shoved down our throats. We know more about us than anybody else. Shouldn't we have some say in plans for our own health? You're damn right we should!"

Like the CAA, the community mental health center and staff must be able to accommodate the personal growth and social change that intervention, including its own, may stimulate.

References

Beiser, M. Poverty, social disintegration, and personality. *Journal of Social Issues*, 1965, *21* (1), 56–78.

Brager, G. New concepts and patterns of service: The mobilization for youth program. In F. Riessman, J. Cohen, & A. Pearl (Eds.), *Mental Health of the Poor*. New York: Free Press, 1964. Pp. 412–421.

Cumming, J., & Cumming, E. *Ego and milieu*. New York: Atherton Press, 1963.

Ferman, L. A., Kornbluh, Joyce L., & Haber, A. (Eds.) *Poverty in America*. Ann Arbor: University of Michigan Press, 1965. Pp. 185–191.

Fishman, J. R., & Solomon, F. Youth and social action: Perspectives on the student sit-in movement. *American Journal of Orthopsychiatry*, 1963, *33*, 872–882.

Gans, H. J. Redefining the settlements function for the war on poverty. *Social Work*, 1964, *9*, 3–12.

Haggstrom, W. C. The power of the poor. In F. Riessman, J. Cohen, & A. Pearl (Eds.), *Mental Health of the Poor*. New York: Free Press, 1964. Pp. 205–223.

Leighton, A. H. Poverty and social change. *Scientific American*, 1965, *212*, 21–26.

Piven, F. Participation of residents in neighborhood community action programs. *Social Work,* 1966, *11,* 73–80.

Reiff, R., & Riessman, F. *The indigenous nonprofessional: A strategy of change in community action and community mental health programs.* Community Mental Health Journal Monograph, No. 1. New York: Behavioral Publications, 1965.

Riessman, F. New approaches to mental health treatment for low-income people. In National Conference on Social Welfare, *Social work practice, 1965.* New York: Columbia University Press, 1965. Pp. 174–187.

Riessman, F., & Hallowitz, E. The neighborhood service center: An innovation in preventive psychiatry. *American Journal of Psychiatry,* 1967, *123,* 1403–1413.

Topeka Office of Economic Opportunity. *Annual report for 1965–1966.* Topeka: OEO, 1966.

Topeka Shawnee Regional Planning Commission. *Neighborhood analysis for the Topeka-Shawnee County Regional Planning Area.* Master Plan Report Number 5, Topeka, 1965.

Wittenberg, R. M. Personality adjustment through social action. *American Journal of Orthopsychiatry,* 1948, *18,* 207–221.

Zurcher, L. A. Functional marginality: Dynamics of a poverty intervention organization. *Southwestern Social Science Quarterly,* 1967, *48,* 56–68.

Zurcher, L. A. The leader and the lost: A case study of indigenous leadership in a poverty program neighborhood action committee. *Genetic Psychology Monograph,* 1967b, *76,* 23–93.

Zurcher, L. A., & Green, A. E., with Johnson, E. & Patton, S. From dependency to dignity: Individual and social consequences of a neighborhood house. New York: Behavioral Publications, 1969.

Zurcher, L. A., & Key, W. H. The overlap model: A comparison of strategies for social change. *Sociology Quarterly,* 1967, *9,* 23–36.

Chapter 2
Urban Renewal and the
Problems of Community Involvement

William H. Key

The mental health effects of forced relocation resulting from urban renewal have been well documented, most notably by Gans[1] and Fried.[2] Since communities are not static entities but constantly changing and developing, some relocation becomes inevitable. However, questions arise as to how urban renewal can be implemented in a manner that would reduce the mental health difficulties that have characteristically arisen when families and individuals have been forced to move from their communities. Dr. Key was hired by the Urban Renewal Agency in Topeka to bring to bear his knowledge on planning and carrying out an urban renewal program consonant with mental health principles. In this article he focuses on the problems arising in gaining acceptance of urban renewal as an aspect of community improvement and relieving the anxieties of some of those groups who were spokesmen for the individuals who were to be displaced. The unique intervention program that followed community acceptance of the renewal program is described in another article by Dr. Key,[3] which forms an excellent supplement to the present chapter.

[1]Gans, H. J. The Urban Villagers. New York: Free Press of Glencoe, 1962.
[2]Fried, M. Transitional functions of working class communities: implications for forced relocation. In Mildred B. Kantor (Ed.), Mobility and mental health. Springfield, Ill.: Charles C Thomas, 1963. Pp. 123–160.
[3]Key, W. H. Controlled intervention—the helping professions and directed social change. American Journal of Orthopsychiatry, 1966, 36, 400–406.

Chapter 2

Urban Renewal and the Problems of Community Involvement

William H. Key

This chapter reports the development of a mental-health oriented relocation program operated by the Topeka Urban Renewal Agency as a part of its "Keyway" project, including a description of the role played by community analysis. Since the development of the relocation program is intertwined with that of the Urban Renewal Agency, no attempt will be made to isolate the development of the relocation program from the history of the agency itself.

First, it is necessary to provide a brief sketch of the community in which the program was carried out. Social change models cannot be understood in a vacuum—that is, a discussion of programs must not include solely a consideration of the intervention program and techniques, but also of the social system in which the program is intervening (Key, 1966; Zurcher & Key, in press).

The Community

Topeka is a stable, slowly growing community, the capital city of the predominantly agricultural state of Kansas. At the time the program was initiated in 1955 the population was approximately 115,000. This population was composed primarily of native-born whites. Ethnic groups who originally migrated to Topeka for farming or railroad employment are rather sparsely represented—8% Negroes; 3.5% Mexican-Americans; and 1% American Indians. The major influx of Negroes came in the 1870's as the result of an "exodus" from Tennessee. At the end of that decade Negroes represented 31% of the population. Few migrate to Topeka now, and their proportion in the population has steadily declined to the present level. Mexicans were first imported by the Santa Fe Railroad to work on the tracks in 1907. Their proportion in the population has been relatively stable during the last few decades.

The economy of Topeka is diversified and stable. The major sources of employment are local, state, and Federal agencies. After World War II extensive psychiatric facilities had been organized around the Menninger Foundation and its School of Psychiatry. The city had attracted some manufacturing plants of national corporations to augment the blue-collar jobs provided by the Santa

Fe Railroad and a number of small home-owned industries. This pattern of economic expansion had brought about an increase in the proportion of both blue-collar and professional groups in the population. The level of education in this population was higher than the national average, the level of unemployment was low, and the average disposable income was somewhat higher than in similar cities across the country.

The community "power structure" was composed of leaders in the financial and business affairs of the community and the professionals, primarily lawyers, who served them. Conservative in outlook, their political rhetoric contained many references to states' rights, rejection of the expansion of the Federal Government, an emphasis on individualism, a rejection of welfare ideology, and a general distaste for the direct use of government to promote socially acceptable ends. The values of these business leaders were mirrored by those of the middle-class majority, and through an interlocking directorate they kept a tight rein on civic affairs.

A more intensive analysis of the socioeconomic conditions somewhat compromises this "all is well" picture. Census tract statistics revealed that some areas had unemployment rates as high as 10% and that in some areas more than 50% of the houses were substandard. In 1955 when urban renewal was initiated the city was just beginning to recover from a reduction in blue-collar employment, which was the aftermath of the disastrous flood of 1951.

Despite these "flaws" there was little if any unrest and virtually no organized protest in the summer of 1955. The civil rights organizations were relatively quiet and virtually unknown to the leaders of the community. One prominent businessman in the late 1950's received a letter from the NAACP threatening to picket his store during the Christmas buying season if more Negroes weren't hired. He had to ask, "Who or what is the NAACP?" The unions, which in other settings were leaders in social change, confined their activities to wage and hour negotiations; and the development of youth protests were still almost a decade in the future. In summary, the community was stable with few if any questions being raised about the status quo.

Establishment of the Urban Renewal Program

Interest in an urban renewal program for Topeka was stimulated when a native Kansan, a former Congressman, and head of the Housing and Home Finance Agency under the Eisenhower Administration, visited in Topeka shortly after his appointment to that position. His discussions of urban renewal with Topeka business and political leaders received considerable local publicity. In these discussions he emphasized the 1954 amendments that liberalized the Urban Renewal Law of 1949 by permitting cities to undertake the renovation of business and industrial areas. These amendments departed from the earlier rehousing and slum clearance orientation by emphasizing the revitalization of renewal of the community's economy.

Following this visit, a movement was started in conjunction with business leaders in other Kansas communities to amend the Kansas statutes to permit urban renewal in Kansas. These efforts were concluded successfully when the 1955 session of the Kansas legislature passed a bill to permit Kansas cities of the first class to engage in urban renewal actions. Later that same year the mayor of Topeka convened a citizens' advisory committee consisting of 35 members to discuss the possibility of Topeka's undertaking an urban renewal project. These citizens were almost exclusively representative of middle-class organizations. Each of the members of this original group were asked to seek out 10 or more acquaintances in his neighborhood or profession and discuss with them the prospect of urban renewal. They were asked to report the reactions of these panels to the mayor at a second session of the advisory committee. At that session, which was held in early 1956, the reactions were glowing as a picture of a revitalized and more beautiful Topeka was painted.

The author of this paper was one of the original advisory committee and had selected a group of fellow faculty members from Washburn University as his panel. His report, while generally supporting the goals of urban renewal, sounded the only pessimistic note when he reported that his panel was concerned about the problems urban renewal would pose for the people in the area and that they did not feel that the impact on the people was being considered adequately. Very little attention was paid to this concern, since other people felt that this was a detail to be dealt with later. The group voted unanimously to urge the mayor and City Commission to initiate urban renewal in Topeka. This group was never reconvened.

The discussion at that and subsequent meetings of business and political leaders emphasized predominantly economic arguments. These arguments were congenial to businessmen, and the raison d'être of the project was publicly presented in terms such as increased tax income for the city, increased employment, increased business and industrial activity, and progress through economic growth. This choice of goals and adjectives neutralized the resistance of community leaders, which might have been expected. Their enthusiasm for community economic betterment allowed some of them to rationalize their involvement with a Federal grant-in-aid program as long as it was endorsed and managed at the national level by a native Kansan and couched in acceptable phrases. In summary, there were three important features of the early established program: (1) The selection of and emphasis on business redevelopment instead of the elimination of housing blight or improvement of the housing of low income people. (2) An emphasis in public statements on the tax gains and economic betterment that the city would realize. (3) The pledge by the original board chairman not to include public housing (a program with a "bad" local reputation) in the relocation plan.

During 1956 the City Commission adopted the required legal resolutions declaring that some areas of slum and blight existed in the city. The City Commission exercised its option of setting up a quasi-independent body, the Topeka Urban Renewal Agency, in lieu of directly exercising the powers granted it by the Kansas Urban Renewal Law. Five businessmen were appointed by the mayor to serve as the governing board of the new agency. The Board of Topeka Urban Renewal Agency hired an executive director and opened an office during the latter part of 1956. In urban renewal language, they became known as the Local Public Agency (LPA), authorized to carry out all of the powers granted to cities under the urban renewal law except designate an area for urban renewal treatment or approve an urban renewal plan. These latter powers were reserved to the City Commission.

A Project Is Planned and a Controversy Develops

A specific geographical area of the city was recommended to the City Commission, and the LPA was authorized to apply to the Federal Urban Renewal Administration for funds to plan a project in the area. These funds were promptly granted, and the area was named "Keyway" to symbolize that this project opened the door to an improved Topeka. Using these funds, the LPA proceeded to gather the information necessary to plan precisely what was to be done to or in the area, i.e., what buildings were to be torn down, what streets to be repaved or rerouted, what new sewers or water lines were to be installed, and what the area was to contain and look like when redevelopment was completed. This highly technical planning was carried out quietly and out of public view except for an occasional newspaper story. These stories usually focused (as they probably must) on the ultimate plan and were illustrated by typical planners' and architects' dreams of what might be.

As part of the planning, the LPA was required by Federal law and regulations to develop a relocation plan that would enable them to relocate residents from the project area into decent, safe, and sanitary housing at prices they could afford to pay. Under Federal regulations this plan had to be based on adequate information about the needs, desires, and resources of the families. To secure this information, the author of this paper was approached by the Topeka Urban Renewal Agency and asked to carry out a survey of the families in the area. He was joined in supervision of the survey by three faculty members from Washburn University. After extensive discussions with LPA personnel and reading of urban renewal literature and manuals, this steering committee devised a satisfactory interview schedule and hired a number of mature law students as interviewers. The contract under which the interviewing was carried out did not include analysis and interpretation of the data, but the field notes of the interviewers were so striking that a final report was prepared (not by the author of this paper) to warn the agency of difficulties that lay ahead. This report emphasized the anxiety, hostility, lack of information, and concern about the future actions of the Urban Renewal Agency on the part of the residents of the project area. The residents viewed urban renewal as something being done to them which they did not understand. The report predicted that relocation was going to be a focal point of concern, contained many potential problems, and should receive concentrated attention. It was received but made no noticeable impact on the operation of the agency.

Shortly after this report was submitted other groups, most notably civil rights, social welfare, and ultraconservative groups, were all raising questions. One of the first public manifestations of this unrest was a seminar for social workers and ministers, sponsored by the Shawnee County Association for Mental Health, the Topeka Welfare Planning Council, and the Topeka Chapter of the National Association of Social Workers. The seminar, "When People Move," discussed the literature on mobility and then focused on urban renewal as a specific case. The seminar ended by drafting an open letter to the Topeka Urban Renewal Agency calling on the agency to give as much serious attention to relocation as it had to real estate, architectural, and engineering matters.

The NAACP, through the efforts of a group of younger Negroes, was also becoming active by sponsoring a series of public meetings to discuss the Keyway Project and particularly the relocation planning. They also launched an active letter-writing campaign directed to the Kansas Congressional delegation, the regional and national offices of the Urban Renewal Administration, and finally to Representatives and Senators from other states, trying to delay approval of the plan until more adequate relocation provisions were included.

Many ministers were also active in their individual churches and through the Council of Churches. Many sermons were preached dealing with the potential problems of the people to be displaced; and the Council of Churches, through its housing and social action committee, kept up a running commentary via bulletins and meetings. One young radio announcer, an ardent civil rights advocate and a critic of urban renewal, organized several panel discussions of the Keyway plan, especially relocation. The tone of virtually all of this public activity was critical of the Urban Renewal Agency for failing to consider adequately in their planning the rehousing and emotional problems of those who were to be displaced.

The LPA Board and staff, not understanding the total social structure of the community and separated from the above named groups by value and communication barriers, continued to address itself to the only public with which it was concerned (or even perceived), namely, the business leaders in the community. The Urban Renewal Agency Board members were not sensitive to the fact that the program would have different meanings for different categories of the population and did not systematically analyze the publics they were addressing.[1]

Closely related to, but not identical to, the problem of analyzing the community was the problem of clogged or ignored lines of communication. The Urban Renewal Agency, concentrating on the technical problems involved in launching its first project, simply "tuned out" these other messages. It would not be correct to say that there was no concern for public relations, since there were numerous stories in the newspapers and brochures were printed and distributed. However, public relations was equated with publicity and the restricted content of the messages. As a result, the failure to achieve closure on the issues important to the groups mentioned and the place and manner of presenting the messages meant that only a small proportion of the population would be reached, and that many would be skeptical. The Urban Renewal Agency had not involved any of the affected people, businessmen or residents, in planning the projects or planning for their displacement. They were doing something for and to people, rather than *with* them. The result of this pattern of operation was that the image projected by the agency was varied, depending on the needs of the perceiving individual and the information he had available, but it was almost consistently negative.

Before the urban renewal plan prepared by the Urban Renewal Agency could be approved, the City Commission was required by law to hold a public hearing. The public hearing was held in February, 1959; and the public concern and criticism that were expressed first in the several meetings mentioned above culminated in a very stormy session at the hearing. Following that hearing the Keyway project became one of the most discussed issues of the city election campaign being held in March of that year. However, the results of the election were ambiguous. Several of the City Commissioners were replaced, but not all of the incoming City Commissioners were clearly anti-urban renewal. However, they were not identified with the present agency, and all had been more or less critical of the Keyway plan, especially the relocation provisions. The Topeka Urban Renewal Agency had been closely identified with the previous City Commission and especially with the mayor, who had chosen not to run for re-election. They were now faced with a skeptical, if not hostile, City Commission, with little support among the citizenry.

The outgoing City Commission, following the public hearing, had agreed to delay approval of the Keyway plan until after April 14 so that the new City Commission could approve or disapprove it. However, under some time pressure from the regional office of the Urban Renewal Administration, they res-

---

[1]Parenthetically, it might be pointed out that this does not constitute a criticism of the board, since there is no more reason that they should analyze these variables than to expect them to be competent architects or lawyers. However, it should be pointed out that the board recognized the usefulness of professional services of architects and attorneys but not that of a community analyst.

cinded this prior action and approved the plan presented at the public hearing as one of their last official acts.

This hasty approval of the plan aroused some intense emotional reactions, and it soon became evident that the opponents of the Keyway project did not intend to drop the matter. During the summer of 1959, two lawsuits were filed challenging the right of the agency to proceed. One suit, which challenged the legitimacy of the designation of the area as slum and blight, was filed in District Court by some businessmen from the project area. The other suit, which challenged the adequacy of the relocation plan for rehousing minority groups, was filed in Federal court by the NAACP on behalf of some project-area residents. Thus, even though the plan had been approved by the City Commission and the Federal Urban Renewal Administration, these two lawsuits and the temporary injunctions which were granted by the courts prevented execution of the plan. Fortunately for the agency, an interstate highway, which would not be affected by the outcome of the legal actions, bisected the Keyway project. Under an agreement with the plaintiffs in the court cases, the agency was permitted to buy property, relocate people, and demolish buildings within the limits of the right-of-way of the highway. This allowed the agency to hold together the staff that had been assembled and to use the staff and time to modify the plan to meet the charges raised by critics.

The Agency Adjusts

The Topeka Urban Renewal Agency was in trouble, and its Governing Board set about rectifying the situation. Their first act in this regard was the appointment of an unbiased, in fact quite critical, relocation advisory committee. The recruitment of members for the committee was carried out jointly by the Topeka Welfare Planning Council and the Urban Renewal Agency. The selection of relocation as the area in which to appoint the first advisory group was significant, since dealing with the residents in the area did not involve the central purpose of the program, but relocation had become the focus for community antagonism.

The first act of the advisory committee was to insist that the agency secure the services of a professional social scientist to assist in the planning and operation of the relocation program. They argued that relocation required as much professional attention as did other parts of the project. Attempts to secure the services of a full-time sociologist or a trained community organization worker failed. Several candidates were approached, and one presented so accurate an assessment of the lack of trust between the Urban Renewal Agency and other community groups that one of the agency board members accused the relocation committee of dictating the assessment with the intent of sabotaging the program. This led to a bitter but cathartic meeting, wherein a consensus was reached that the Keyway project could not proceed without some additional consideration of the human implications of relocation. Finally, at the suggestion of a member of the advisory committee, the vice president for academic affairs of Washburn University was approached; and the services of the author of this paper were secured on a part-time basis. That appointment was important because it symbolized for the committee and the public a willingness on the part of the Urban Renewal Agency to meet reasonable criticism with positive rather than defensive action.

The first task facing the social science consultant was to perform three functions for the board members of the agency: (1) to analyze the community, differentiate the various publics that were related to Urban Renewal, and to describe their attitudes; (2) to analyze the actions of the agency that had contributed to the negative attitudes on the part of the various publics; and (3) to recommend some specific actions that would counter the opposition that had developed, including advising the agency how to reconstruct the relocation plan. Understandably, the Urban Renewal Agency Commissioners had been hurt and confused when, after four years of public-spirited, time-consuming work, they had received few public accolades, instead primarily abuse, anger, and insults. They were genuinely interested in building a better Topeka and were serving in almost every case at a considerable sacrifice.[2]

One of the first acts of the consulting social scientist was to prepare an analysis of the community, defining the relevant groups, suggesting how they viewed the agency, and suggesting appropriate actions to meet the criticisms. Much of the material in the remainder of this section is taken from that memo, which was prepared in late 1959 and which served as *one* basis for later operational decisions.[3]

The Urban Renewal Agency was viewed by most of the businessmen in the community with mixed emotions. They saw it as serving a potentially useful

[2]As usual, there were suspicions of exploitation and direct profittaking by members of the board and their friends. Rumors of wrongdoing were widely disseminated, and "inside" stories of how this person or that one made a "killing" out of the Keyway Project were numerous. However, all such efforts to understand the course of events are much too simpleminded, as well as being without foundation in fact. No hint of scandal has ever touched the operation of the Topeka Urban Renewal Agency; and in eight years of close scrutiny, the author can vouch for the scrupulous honesty of board members. Because the board members were businessmen with diverse interests in the city, the normal operation of their business life presented many opportunities to make money out of Urban Renewal; but to my knowledge they were, without exception, rejected. However, our point here is not the personal morality or honesty of the board members but to suggest that the events described in this paper have to be understood as a result of social and sociopsychological processes and conditions rather than the personal character of the people involved.

[3]The extensive use of the memo in this paper is not intended to exaggerate its role or influence in this community drama. However, its contents do reflect many discussions with urban renewal personnel, relocation advisory committee members, and interested private citizens. In addition, it served as an important source document for this chapter, a document not subject to the vagaries of memory.

function in upgrading the economy of the community, but run inefficiently with too much idealism and not enough "hardheaded" business sense. Many of them were uneasy about urban renewal because they feared that this was part of a trend toward socialism. They were not sure whether the benefits would outweigh the liabilities, but on balance were in favor of the Keyway project.

The Urban Renewal Agency presented no clear-cut image to the middle-class members of the community. They did not understand the purposes, procedures, assets, or liabilities. They tended to react negatively to the emphasis on money advantages, since they failed to see a pay-off for any except a small group. Many of them found it difficult to countenance the use of governmental power to transfer property from one private owner to another, no matter what community good resulted.

The liberals and intellectuals of the community were outraged by what they viewed as a perversion of the intent of the legislation—to help the slum-dwellers. They felt a lack of morality or idealism on the part of the agency, were antagonistic over the relocation program, and were little impressed with the "business advantages" cited by agency personnel as the major goals of the project. "Heartless," "cruel," "scheming," and "selfish" were some of the adjectives used. They have tended to be moved more by ideas than by pleas to the pocketbook and had yet to find a basis on which to support urban renewal.

The image of the agency held by the lower class was not clear. Typically this segment of the local population had felt very little involvement in the community. They felt as if they were being manipulated wherever they were located. They resented direct interference in their lives but were not (in 1959) vocal, organized, or effective in support of or in opposition to programs. They were most important in this project for two reasons:

1. Numerically, this was a very large group. If a vote were ever taken, they could make or break the program.
2. They were the people most directly involved.

These people in the area were afraid of what would happen to them and plagued by uncertainty as to the time their property would be acquired and the amount they would be reimbursed for their property. They could see that some of the people in the area were going to be hurt and felt that there was no recognition for their difficulties and/or an indifference to their problems.

Minority groups could have been included in several of the other categories but deserve special mention because they were organized. They, specifically the NAACP, were in favor of urban renewal because they viewed it as a potential tool for improving their housing opportunities. They very much wanted to see the Urban Renewal Agency succeed. However, in 1959 and 1960 they felt that the Urban Renewal Agency outlook was representative of existing white attitudes toward segregation. Thus, it was hard to class Negroes as a group opposing urban renewal, since they were potentially supporters and their opposition was based almost entirely on their frustration in trying to communicate the needs of Negroes to the Urban Renewal Agency Board and its staff.

The City Commission, which took office in April of 1959, was an enigma. Urban renewal had been much discussed during the election, but it was hard to classify the members of the City Commission as for or against the Keyway project—good politicians that they were. Since their term of office was only two years and they would soon face re-election, it was clear that they were swayed more by their interpretations of the effect of urban renewal on their political fortunes than by any beliefs. They had no direct control over the program, since the Urban Renewal Commission was a quasi-independent body; but they could, by their support or lack of it, determine the ultimate success of the project.

The major identified source of public opposition to the principle of urban renewal rather than the Keyway project was the Topeka Property Owners Association and the Topeka Taxpayers Association. These groups, who overlapped in membership, represented the ultraconservative viewpoint in Topeka. They had been able to rally support beyond their own small numbers because Topeka is a politically conservative town, and there was latent opposition to this "radical" program. They had been active in the spring city election campaign and were feeling confident. They had two main bases of opposition. Overtly, they worked to hold down taxes and restrict the growth of government. Covertly, some of the most active members owned substandard rental housing in the area, and they dreaded losing this profitable property. They were a small but important group because they were organized and could serve as a vehicle to focus some of the scattered opposition.

Assuming the accuracy of the foregoing assessment, what actions of the agency had contributed to its difficulties and what actions could it take to insure its survival? Some of the behavior of the agency has been suggested earlier, so this is only a summary.

1. *The emphasis on taxes and business advantages.*

2. *The apparent lack of concern over the impact on people.* The specific actions were a refusal to survey housing resources available for relocation purposes and a rejection of public housing before the housing needs were known.

3. *The vagueness of the plan.* In relocation promises to individualize treatment were viewed as a way to escape responsibility for developing a satisfactory relocation plan. The rules and procedures for buying land from present owners and for reselling the land after it was cleared had not been published in detail. These ambiguities contributed to a feeling that something was being "put over."

4. *The program of separateness.* Agency personnel largely stayed in the office working at the planning task and had the minimum number of contacts with outside agencies or groups. The Agency was out of contact with public opinion, and they were an unknown quantity to many of the individuals and groups with whom they had to work.

5. *The circumstances under which the project was approved.* The Keyway plan was approved as

one of the last official acts of a lame duck City Commission. In view of all of the signs of opposition, this encouraged the feeling that there was something unsavory about the project.

From the summer of 1959 to the end of 1960, much of the energy of the personnel associated with the Topeka Urban Renewal Agency was dedicated to insuring its survival. During that period many procedural and attitudinal changes were made. The agency was reorganized internally and streamlined for greater efficiency. A set of job descriptions was developed, an internal communication system was established, the accounting system was overhauled, and the operating procedures were modernized. All of the previous plans were reviewed and updated with additional data. The plans were rewritten in more specific and concrete language. As part of this activity, the relocation workers began a series of extensive interviews with residents of the area about their needs, desires, and resources. This information was used to update the older survey, as a basis for developing a relocation plan for each household and as the basis for a revised relocation plan.

The program of separateness was ended. All meetings became open meetings, with the press and the City Commission receiving special invitations and advance agendas. Advisory committees were appointed in the areas of public relations and redevelopment, in addition to the relocation advisory committee, which had been appointed earlier. An information campaign was launched among the residents of the project area, and several project area residents were appointed to serve on the advisory committees. One might say that a program of "maximum feasible participation" was begun five years before the poverty program. Speaking engagements at service clubs were increased in number and variety. Contacts with other agencies in the community were initiated, and their assistance and advice sought.

The concentration on economic gains and the lack of attention to the problems of the people to be moved ended. The most active advisory committee remained the Citizens' Relocation Advisory Committee (CRAC), and the agency hired an executive director to help it with its work. CRAC now included people from the project area, as well as a wide variety of representatives from other institutions and agencies. It joined with the Urban Renewal Agency's relocation division in systematically analyzing the relocation needs, matching those needs with the resources available and writing a plan that took into account both needs and resources. The total relocation program, which has been described in detail elsewhere (Key, 1967), included the use of nonprofessional helpers, an aggressive reaching out to clients rather than an office-bound program, and an adoption of an ombudsman orientation and operation rather than shifts in details of the program.

The major program shift was the inclusion of public housing. Based on the analysis mentioned above, CRAC and the relocation division came to the conclusion that public housing was the only reasonable way to guarantee satisfactory relocation of approximately one-fourth of the project area residents. The Urban Renewal Agency Board accepted the public housing recommendation and personally "sold" it in a series of meetings to the three parts of the "power structure" that might have vetoed it—the Chamber of Commerce, the Real Estate Board, and the Contractors Association. This was a major shift, since public housing had been rejected previously by the board without knowing the dimensions of the relocation problem. This change in the attitude of the board and their use of the hard data of research as a basis for decision-making began to restore confidence in the agency among some of the most critical groups.

Opposition and Final Resolution

The changes that had been and were being made had gone far to satisfy the demands of those who were not against urban renewal in general but who did oppose the Keyway plan that had been presented at the February, 1959, public hearing. However, the ultraconservative groups were still active and still opposed to all urban renewal. They had been active in the 1959 city elections and had received a considerable amount of encouragement as a result of the general dissatisfaction with the Keyway plan. During the latter part of 1959 and the first half of 1960, they continued their public meetings, criticizing urban renewal and demanding a popular vote on the program.

During this period they launched a campaign to secure a vote by narrowing their attack to the method of financing the city's share. They circulated a petition requesting that the City Commission place the question of financing on the ballot in the August, 1960, primary elections. The city's share of the cost of the Keyway project was to be financed under a "pay-as-you-go" plan, with approximately one-fifth of the total cost coming out of the general budget of the city each year of the expected five-year span of the project. An alternative method of financing that had been considered during the planning but rejected because of its expense was to issue bonds to be repaid over a much longer period of time. Since Topeka had fewer than 125,000 people at that time, a bond issue required a popular vote. The petitioners reasoned that a vote against the bonds would be viewed as an indirect vote against urban renewal. An adequate number of signatures was obtained, and the petitions were filed with the City Commission. Due to the form in which the petitions were presented, it was not mandatory that the City Commission acquiesce in the request; but in July, 1960, they had placed on their agenda for the next meeting a resolution that would have placed the question of urban renewal financing on the August ballot.

The question arose among the agency and board members of whether it would be better to take a position or to remain apolitical. Their position was difficult, since they did not approve of the bond method of financing; but if the public and the political leaders interpreted a defeat for the bonds as a rejection of urban renewal, their position would be precarious. A decision was reached that the agency should reiterate its previous position and come out in favor of a negative vote on the bonds. The chairman of the board released a statement urging a negative vote and pointing to the advantages of "pay-as-you-go." The press release treated the election as a straightforward question of financing. This press release redefined the situation, and the agency was put on the public record as interpreting a *no* vote as support for the Topeka Urban Renewal Agency. The City Commission removed the matter from their agenda, and no election was ever held.

From that time opposition declined. The hard-core opposition of the ultra-conservatives had been broken, and the continued working of the agency with a variety of groups had mollified the opposition to specific parts of the Keyway plan. The amended plan, which reduced the size of the project area, eliminated the portion in which the businessmen who had challenged the designation of slum and blight were located. The amended relocation plan, worked out in conjunction with many civic groups, contained a public housing provision that eliminated the objections of the NAACP. The amended plan was presented at another public hearing in February, 1961, almost exactly two years after the first Keyway plan had been presented. Shortly after that the two lawsuits were dismissed, the new plan was adopted by the City Commission, and approved by the Federal Urban Renewal Administration.

Aftermath

By the end of 1960 the issue was decided. Urban renewal was to survive. It had gained the necessary community support and has continued to exist and become an accepted part of the community—controversial at times but increasingly used by those interested in community betterment. The particular project described in this section survived in a somewhat altered form. Started as a real estate venture, of interest primarily to businessmen concerned about taxes and economic growth, it shifted to include as a concern the problems of the people who lived in the area. The Urban Renewal Agency and the professionals it hired in conjunction with a representative group of citizens developed what was at that time the most extensive and sophisticated relocation program in the region—a program guided largely by social psychiatric and social science theory.

This urban renewal project served as a vehicle for community integration through community conflict. Ultimately, all of the community groups who were interested saw some of their goals accomplished through urban renewal, except the ultraconservatives and the slum landlords. New lines of communications were opened that have continued to serve community interests. For example, the NAACP went into the fight with the two major goals of public housing and an open occupancy ordinance. They got public housing and the opening of some new residential areas to Negroes. They did not get an open occupancy ordinance. However, there were side benefits, according to one of the leaders of the NAACP fight with urban renewal. In a recent interview, reviewing those early days, he said:

> The NAACP received a great deal of admiration and sympathy from an unexpected quarter. Many businessmen in and out of the Keyway area were opposed to Urban Renewal for a number of economic reasons. In addition, some of them bitterly resented the fact that the businesses they had built up over the years should suddenly have to make way for big business, and some felt that city government had no right to arbitrarily declare an area blighted for the purpose of seizing control. Some businessmen who had been traditionally opposed to the goals of the NAACP grew to admire the NAACP for its courage in fighting the heavy hand of the government. Until the businessmen became interested, no other organization except the NAACP had taken any public stand with respect to the Keyway Urban Renewal Project. This association of the businessmen and the NAACP led to good relationships that were mutually fruitful in other areas. This was the first effective line of communication between these two groups in the City of Topeka, and it has continued to serve us since that time.

In one sense this project was a model for community action. It was proposed and operated by an "upper class" group who were oblivious to the meaning urban renewal had for other portions of the community. However, the project touched the lives of many people in the community; and the initiators were forced to modify their plans in confrontation with people lower in the hierarchy. It should be noted that the conflict remained focused on issues and not on personalities. During this very long period, some people in key positions were replaced; but personalities were never publicly involved. Personal integrity was respected. In this confrontation, at least some of the demands of all the "legitimate" groups were met.

The conflict which seemed so difficult and threatening at times proved to be beneficial to the community and to the project. The debates, disagreements, and delays that marked the slow progress of the Keyway project led to the involvement of almost all of the interested parties in the decision-making process. New lines of communication were opened between people who had scarcely spoken in previous years, and at least some of these channels are still being utilized in the decision-making process in Topeka. Diverse types of people learned to work together for a common goal and were mutually educated about each other. New opportunities for participation in decision-making were extended to people never before so involved. There are many compromises, but this seems the essence of community development. It is when the situation degenerates into demands for "all or nothing" that community development ends and revolution begins.

The conflict proved to be beneficial for the Keyway project as well. The debates and disagreements were the "birth pangs" of a new force in the community. If one may view the period from the fall of 1956 to the fall of 1959 as the gestation period, then the period from the fall of 1959 to the winter of 1961 was time spent in the delivery room. This long period in the delivery room attests to the difficulties in the birth of a new program. It also explains why urban renewal is a healthy adolescent at the present time. The fact that a new program is established without debate probably means only that the birth pangs are delayed. It does not mean that the ultimate debate over the program has been avoided. Another way of stating it is that the political process was not short circuited, and urban renewal in Topeka is now the stronger for it. To corrupt a well-known phrase, the ends were justified by the means.

The Keyway project was, as are all such projects, unique. Still, the conclusions with which we end this description are distressingly familiar ones. Focus on the details of the program of a project should not be allowed to replace or "short-circuit" the process by which it is implemented. The way in which a community project is implemented is as important as the nature of the program. "Maximum feasible participation" of all of the interested "legitimate" groups should be encouraged and has positive benefits for both the participant and the community. This participation, undoubtedly, will lead to conflict. However, we should "recognize the social functions of the non-violent conflict and assume that such conflict is an expected by-product of and can be a stimulus to ameliorative social change" (Zurcher & Key, in press). The power of the "establishment" is limited by organization and concerted action of nonestablishment groups. The "power structure" is an open rather than a closed system. In a rapidly changing society there is a role for a community analyst who can develop an objective picture of the community and identify the social processes that are occurring. One important task of such an analyst can be to define, interpret, and translate the issues, and operating as a marginal man between the groups provide a mirror to reflect back to the groups what they are doing. Social change (reform if you prefer) can originate within the system.

References

Key, W. H. Controlled intervention—the helping professions and directed social change. *American Journal of Orthopsychiatry*, 1966, 36, 400–409.

Key, W. H. *When people are forced to move.* Topeka, Kansas: Division of Social Science Research, The Menninger Foundation, 1967.

Zurcher, L. A., & Key, W. H. The overlap model: A comparison of strategies for social change. *Sociology Quarterly*, 1968, 9, 85–96.

Chapter 3
Midway: A Case Study of
Community Organization Consultation

Dwight W. Rieman

It is generally accepted that mental health services are most effective when they are not imposed upon a community (as, for example, in the classic study of the failure of a mental health education program[1]) but generated from community action. The community, with adequate consultation, is able to evaluate its needs, develop a plan, set priorities, and work out problems of implementation. The mental health consultant can serve as a catalyst to the process, helping as a resource person and as one well acquainted with the realities governing the adequate development of mental health services. It is only out of such a collaboration that what is developed can weather the crises that may arise. Mr. Rieman describes in detail how this process took place in a community that became aware of its need for mental health services but required considerable help in order to translate this need into action.

[1]Cumming, E., & Cumming, J. *Closed ranks: An experiment in mental health education.* Cambridge, Mass.: Harvard University Press, 1957.

Chapter 3

Midway: A Case Study of Community Organization Consultation

Dwight W. Rieman

No detailed discussion of community organization is offered, but some working definition is needed to show the relationship between community organization and community organization consultation, which is the central concern of this chapter. *Community organization* is both a field of activity and an enabling process utilized by workers engaged in planning varied health and welfare services. As a process, community organization is concerned with the purpose and method by which people (with or without professional help) join together out of concern about a particular problem, study its scope and dimensions, and plan ways of meeting the problem, including mobilization of necessary community effort and funds (McNeil, 1954; Murphy, 1957).

Community organization consultation is a helping and educational process achieved through a working relationship with citizen and professional leaders to help them carry out the necessary community organization tasks to accomplish the objectives they have set. The community organization consultant assists with the process, but he is not directly a part of it as are the strategic persons in the community who do the organizational work—from the initial point of concern, through appraisal of the problem(s), and finally establishment of appropriate services.

The kind, quality and depth of relationship that the community organization consultant is able to establish and maintain with community leaders may be the most important single ingredient in the helping process. As with other kinds of consultation, community organization consultation is based on authority of ideas and leaves the community leaders, who actually carry out the community organization activities, free to reject or accept, according to their best judgment, the consultant's suggestions (Rieman, 1963).

The community organization consultation experience to be described is based on the belief that community services are most successfully organized and operated when they develop out of local concern and are administratively autonomous, rather than imposed. The state government or other source of consultative and/or financial help should act as a partner in helping to interpret quality services, establish standards, and explain the conditions necessary to maintain and operate services so as to make them available and meaningful to all persons in need of them.

Timeliness

Planning and implementation of community and regional services in public health, mental health, mental retardation, vocational rehabilitation, and related services are currently underway on an extensive scale throughout the country. The process by which services are designed and organized, and the way consultation is provided to communities in helping them to define their objectives and realize their goals varies tremendously. In some places it is a carefully planned process that utilizes, to the maximum, community organization and consultation principles and procedures. In other places it is a rather haphazard process.

Community organization of mental health and mental retardation services is not, as yet, a carefully systematized process. Much more experience with built-in evaluation is required before a "how-to-do-it" manual can be written that will cover the necessary procedural steps for community organization of services and the most desirable patterns of consultation.

Need for Sharing Experiences

Community programs and services in mental health and mental retardation have received considerable attention in the literature. However, descriptions of method by which programs and services are planned and developed, especially those that result from extensive community involvement as compared to state or federally organized and operated services and programs, are still quite rare.

Consultants and others responsible for assisting communities in planning and development of services must record, describe, and share experiences if community organization consultation is to become a refined and disciplined process. Case material, including the "process recorded" variety, which has been so useful in social work training and supervision, should be adapted and utilized in community organization consultation, not only as a means of improving practice, but as a way of providing teaching and training aids.

The dearth of recorded material and analysis in relation to community organization consultation with the *smaller community* is particularly acute. Attention to the smaller community is also especially timely in view of the fact that regional development of comprehensive mental health, retardation, and related health services must give increasing attention to community and regional development of services—*outside of the larger metropolitan areas.* Larger metropolitan areas, with an abundance of consultation and planning resources, undertake planning and implementation tasks differently; and the consultant working with them does not need to wear as many hats as he does in work with the smaller community.

A case example of community organization consultation with a community of *under 50,000 population* is presented. It includes a description of the setting from which the request came, the problem for which help was sought, definition of the problem, and the process leading toward resolution of the problem—in this instance the development of a new service that also stimulated the development of several other services. In fact, the mental health services—a primary concern—came into operation after several other services were established. But some of the steps in the development of the mental health service aided substantially in the establishment of other services—public health, child welfare, and probation. The example also illustrates several roles that a "consultant" operating under auspices of a state department[1] carries out in work with a community, and some of the problems that accompany frequent and sometimes rapid "changing of hats."

Ingredients for Effective Community Organization Consultation

Some ingredients for consultation are offered, before proceeding with description of community organization consultation with a particular community. They are derived from consultation experience devoted to assisting communities, both large and small, in problem definition, appraisal and organization, and extension of needed services. Core ingredients for effective consultation and appropriate community action include:

1. Problem definition and appraisal.
2. Location and development of competent local leadership.
3. Coordination of organization efforts.
4. Consultation relationship built on acceptance, mutual respect, and freedom of operations of both consultant and consultee.
5. Local involvement in depth in problem appraisal, development of priorities, and implementation of services.
6. Establishing appropriate limits and boundaries.
7. Establishing both short- and long-term objectives.
8. Identification of and opportunity to successfully carry out time-limited tasks that are consistent with long-range planning and objectives.

[1]The state department and the consultant's sponsor in this instance was first the Division of Mental Health, Texas State Department of Health. Subsequent legislative action in September, 1965, combined institutional and community service programs in a new department, the Texas Department of Mental Health and Mental Retardation. Responsibility for mental health consultation to the community described continued from the new department.

The writer (and consultant) was Chief Psychiatric Social Worker, Texas Department of Health, during the initial phases of consultation and later Administrative Consultant within the new department's Division of Community Services. He accepts full responsibility for the description, opinions, and interpretations provided in this chapter. The views expressed are those of the writer and not necessarily those of the Texas Department of Health or the Texas Department of Mental Health and Mental Retardation.

These ingredients are certainly not exhaustive, and they are presented in outline form only to help pinpoint some of the elements that were part of a successful community organization and community organization consultation process in the case example that follows.

The major description of the consultant's interaction with citizen and professional leadership covers a five-year period—1960 to 1965. Briefer description of subsequent developments is also provided.

Midway

A Glance at the Community

Midway[2] is located between two considerably larger cities—one about 40 miles to the east in a neighboring state; the other 70 miles to the west. Of the total county population of approximately 45,000 persons (1960), 28,000 reside in the city of Midway. The population is almost evenly divided between Negro and white. The area was once farming and plantation country primarily, but it is difficult now, as one resident pointed out, "to find one little ole cotton patch." Much of the land that was farmed is now used for grazing purposes or developed for timber. There are several fairly large industries, including two connected with missile production and space exploration. There are two small colleges.

In 1960 there was marked poverty of community services for troubled people. At the time the request came for consultation, there was no child welfare unit, no family agency, no probation officer. There was no public health department, and no psychiatric services. The nearest psychiatrist was located 25 miles away. The nearest publicly supported outpatient mental health facility for which children and adults in Midway were eligible for service was located several hundred miles away. The nearest state hospital for the mentally ill was 75 miles distant.

Action-Motivation and Direction

The request for consultation originated out of concern about juvenile delinquency and other youth problems. The wife of a physician who had served on both the Governor's and White House Conference Committees on Children and Youth had read a pamphlet published by the office that sponsored the consultant's services. The pamphlet is concerned with professional counseling services and a juvenile delinquency prevention project (Stern, 1959).

[2]The name "Midway" is fictitious, but the description of the community is factual. Names of persons and other information of a confidential nature have not been included. The events, persons, and process as portrayed are real and described as accurately as is humanly possible.

The interest of this woman, plus that of a special committee set up by the Chamber of Commerce to study problems of youth, led to a letter of request from the chairman of the "organizational committee." The letter requested that the division [3] send a consultant to "set up community youth services similar to those in Brazos County" (as described in the pamphlet).

The consultant's first trip to Midway was in May, 1960. From then until April, 1965, when formalized mental health services were initiated, the consultant made 15 visits of one to two days each to the community. He was assisted by a research consultant [4] on three of the trips, in helping community leaders to design and carry out a self-survey of mental health and related problems and resources.

For the first meeting attended by the consultant, the chairman had assembled a group with representation from the local mental health association, welfare office, Kiwanis Club, two industries, several churches, the Chamber of Commerce, the Employment Commission, Vocational Rehabilitation Office, public schools, American Association of University Women, and the Medical Auxiliary. Following the chairman's description of some of their concerns, about youth particularly, he introduced the consultant with instructions to *"tell us what to do."*

The consultant talked briefly about kinds and estimated distributions of mental health problems in communities, generally, along with a discussion of some possible approaches to these problems in the way of preventive, educational, counseling, and treatment services. For a major part of the meeting the consultant encouraged group members to discuss the kinds of emotional problems that they observed in the community, the kinds of services available in the community to help, and the services they would like to see developed. This was a good learning experience as a whole, as many learned for the first time how others viewed emotional problems in their particular organizational or work setting.

In this and subsequent meetings, it became apparent that some of this group, including the chairman and several other prominent citizens, had some fairly definite ideas about a service that they wanted to establish. This was patterned after similar services in one or more cities in a neighboring state, and in essence consisted of a citizens' youth advisory board made up of one or more businessmen, an educator, physician, minister, lawyer, etc. The board met at regular intervals to hear personal problems concerning youth or adults, or both, and then advice was given as to what should be done. The chairman of the organiza-

[3]Division of Mental Health, Texas State Department of Health, Charles F. Mitchell, ACSW, Director; now Assistant Professor, University of Missouri, School of Social Work, Columbia.
[4]Fred R. Crawford, Ph.D., former Research Consultant, Division of Mental Health, Texas State Department of Health; now Director of the Center for Research in Social Change, Thompson Hall, Emory University, Atlanta.

tional committee in Midway thought that, in the absence of other services and the presence of much youth in trouble, such a board could provide a useful service in their community. The consultant explained that from his understanding of the proposal such a service might not work very well, especially without professional supervision, and said also that it could not take the place of a professional service.[5]

The consultant suggested that it might be well to have several more meetings (with wider representation from the community) to discuss additional problems and concerns. In addition, he suggested that before they moved toward establishment of a specific service, it might be a good idea to take a systematic look at overall needs and resources. He mentioned a *community self-survey guide* (Division of Mental Health, Texas State Department of Health, 1963) which his office was developing and offered, if they were interested, to provide a limited amount of consultation in helping them to carry out a self-survey.

The group had several meetings before the consultant's second visit, which occurred about three months later. The committee had been expanded, additional problems were discussed, and the idea of a self-survey was explored. Also, before the consultant's second visit, the film *Community Mental Health* (Mental Health Film Board, 1959) was shown, as suggested by the consultant because of its attention to survey of community mental health needs and process of organizing for action toward development of needed services.

During the consultant's second visit the committee discussed a community self-survey. In general the group favored the idea. There were some, however, who felt this was not necessary. They "knew" what the problems were; the Citizens' Youth Advisory Board as discussed earlier would answer the problems satisfactorily; or the problems in Midway were not really of such severity as to warrant the establishment of any *new* service.

Some of the "dissenters" removed themselves from the committee, but a core group of interested persons remained. Leadership within the group began to emerge. Although there were many changes in composition of the basic group in the months and years ahead, the "group within the group" that really kept things moving remained intact.

Community Self-Survey

Together with a survey of emotional problems in various age groups, a limited sampling of attitudes and opinions was carried out among care-giving per-

[5]In this and later group and individualized sessions with the chairman and others, discussion continued regarding services provided by a citizens' advisory board, as compared with a professionally directed service. The consultant recognized with them that advice from such a group, as from one's personal friends, could be of value at times. But the counter-argument he presented (which apparently was the most convincing in support of a professional service) was that knowledge of personal or family problems of a highly confidential nature might also be viewed or handled unwisely by business, religious, or other community associates unskilled in the "helping" process.

sonnel and community leaders concerning needs for services, directions the community should take in coordination of existing services, extent of help currently available for work with troubled people, new services that should be developed, etc.

Although the survey instruments had many flaws, their use in the community proved to be effective in stimulating action. The basic survey team consisted of 25 people, but the total number of persons involved in the survey, write-up, and preparation of recommendations numbered more than 50.

Almost 100% of physicians (23) and ministers (28) in the community were interviewed. In addition, many of the attorneys and law enforcement officials were contacted, as were representatives from numerous other public and private organizations—home demonstration agents, general hospital personnel, and representatives from state and federal organizations with offices in the community.

Much of the information was gathered through direct interviews, and this proved to be a tremendously valuable educational experience for the surveyors and others. They discussed their findings, not only with survey committee members, but with business colleagues, their families, and members or organizations to which they belonged. Before the survey was even completed an important part of the educational task in the community had already been accomplished.

The statistics were quantitatively impressive to the surveyors. But it was actually the "personalization" of statistics through description that seemed to convey most meaning and that was most significant in motivating the surveyors to prod the community into action. Most of the surveyors, although somewhat overwhelmed with what they learned, were quite enthusiastic about their tasks and the need to develop and extend services for troubled people in the community.

Consultation Approach and Committee Recommendations

The consultation approach, both during initial work with the steering committee and throughout the survey process and analysis, was one directed toward helping the community look in a systematic way at the wide range of human problems and the relatedness of youth and adult problems. The consultant attempted to make clear from the first that although he represented a public mental health organization, his mission was not necessarily that of helping this community organize a mental health service. If, following their study, this seemed indicated, then of course he and his sponsoring organization would help in any way they could toward this end. If, however, other types of helping services for troubled people seemed of higher priority, the consultant agreed to help them locate specialized consultants from other appropriate fields.

The survey findings, as could be expected in a community so devoid of professional helping services, pointed toward needs for many kinds of services. Prominent among these were child welfare, probation, strengthening of counseling and social work programs in the public schools, psychiatric services for children and adults, mental health consultation and inservice training, and public health services.

Before the steering committee established priorities and recommendations for services, the consultant helped them to:

1. Study the various types of services as outlined above.
2. Arrange direct contacts with specialists from fields other than mental health.

This seemed particularly important in this community that had no professional social work services and no community planning council. For most on the steering committee, and the community at large, the only contact they had with a professional social worker up to this point was the one with the consultant.

The consultant helped them to obtain study materials, and the committee reviewed various types of services. They also viewed and discussed a number of films describing these services. In addition, they arranged, at the consultant's suggestion, to meet with a consultant from the National Council on Crime and Delinquency. They also, as suggested by the consultant, received consultation from the Division of Child Welfare, Texas State Department of Welfare, and from the Division of Local Health Services, Texas State Department of Health, concerning the functions, costs, and staffing of child welfare and public health services respectively.

Along with other types of services that the committee studied and considered before making recommendations was a *family guidance and consultation center.* This was a medically oriented and supervised mental health service designed by the consultant and his colleagues. The design was particularly adapted for the smaller community, with a proposed division of *service* time roughly as follows: 50% for direct services to children and adults; and 50% for consultation, inservice training, community organizations, and evaluation. Staff: two full-time social workers (at least one with some seasoning in administration, consultation, and community organization); one psychiatrist for a minimum of one day per week; one psychologist for a minimum of two days per month. The psychiatrist in this proposal was to be responsible both for medical supervision and direct services as needed.

The steering committee in its considerations was encouraged by the consultant to determine not only what *type* of service should have first priority as far as needs were concerned, but also to consider what professional service might have widest *community acceptance and support.* Following study of the various services and conferences with specialized consultants from several fields, as outlined earlier, the steering committee decided on the following priority:

1. Family guidance and consultation center.
2. Juvenile probation service.
3. Public health department.
4. Child welfare unit.
5. Community planning council.

Training and Interpretation

Before submitting their report to the Chamber of Commerce and other interested groups (approximately one year following the consultant's first visit to Midway), and also before community-wide interpretation was attempted, the steering committee and some other interested individuals (who were later to assist with the community interpretation responsibility) met with the consultant for three two-hour training sessions. The training objectives were to:

1. Develop further insights into what is involved in a professional service to troubled people.
2. Enlarge understanding of a specific mental health service—the Family Guidance and Consultation Center—so that they could do an effective interpretation of the service with various individuals and groups with whom they would be meeting.
3. Provide, through informal discussion, an opportunity for *feeling* or emotional reactions to the material presented and the tasks ahead—as well as for intellectual or academic reactions and discussion.
4. Think together regarding strategy and methods for public interpretation and discussion leadership with a variety of community groups.

The training sessions were attended by the chairman of the steering committee, a faculty member at one of the local colleges, the district attorney, director of the Employment Commission, the county judge, the civic affairs chairman of the Chamber of Commerce, the manager of the Chamber of Commerce, a member of the personnel staff of a local industry, a member of the medical auxiliary, a member of the American Association of University Women, a school counselor, the wife of the administrative director of the local medical society. Four of the 12 in attendance were women.

The discussions centered first of all around further discussion of their survey findings, the needs for professional services, and the priorities that the steering committee had established. Purposes of the training sessions were discussed, including the importance of not "overselling" the proposed Family Guidance and Consultation Center. Concepts and principles of human behavior[6] were presented by the consultant and discussed by the group.

Presentation and discussion of these concepts and work principles were supplemented with the introduction, showing, and discussion of three films. The

[6]For an outline of "principles of behavior" and "work principles in the helping process" (as presented to this and other groups involved in organization and/or provision of helping services for troubled people), see Rieman, D. W., *Mental Health in the Community Public Health Program,* The Hogg Foundation for Mental Health, University of Texas, Austin 78712, 1962, pp. 29–31.

consultant offered a choice of five. Following his summary of each, the group selected these: *Face of Youth* (University of Wisconsin, 1952), *Family Affair* (Mental Health Film Board, 1955), and *Head of the House* (Mental Health Film Board, 1953). As noted earlier, *Community Mental Health* had been used during some preliminary committee work. It had been shown and discussed without assistance from the consultant, other than the suggestion that they might find it useful at that point in their study and deliberations.

The group, with the consultant's help, related the theoretical concepts and the complementary film material to the survey findings, priorities they had established, and the interpretive and organizational tasks ahead of them. The consultant was much more concerned about the brief time available for training (six hours) to cover the breadth and depth of the material than was the group, although some of them recognized the need for additional time if it could have been arranged. However, in viewing the composition of the group, their work and family responsibilities, the amount of time some of them had already spent in the survey and study efforts, it was probably unrealistic to expect this or any other similar group to set aside more time for such a training effort.

Procedural Plan and Timetable

The committee, with the consultant's help, worked out a tentative plan and timetable for their organizational work, including:

1. Reports to the Chamber of Commerce, the Medical Association, and other groups to interpret the recommendations and solicit endorsement and support from these strategic groups.
2. Development of a "prospectus" for the proposed service, to be discussed, revised as needed, and endorsed by the Medical Association and fund sources.
3. Public interpretation and fund raising.
4. Organization of a board of directors.
5. Recruitment of staff.
6. Ongoing collaborative work of the board with professional staff of the center and the community at large.

By local decision, there was to be parallel work on the organization of a probation service. This responsibility, however, was to be carried primarily by the county judge and the district attorney, and not by this committee.

Steps 1, 2, and 3 were carried out according to plan. The County Medical Association endorsed the proposal for a Family Guidance and Consultation Center, and similar endorsements were made by a number of strategic organizations. Budget was discussed with city and county officials, private foundations, and other potential sources of funds.

Parallel Developments and Problems

The consultant learned from personnel in the Division of Local Health Services, Texas State Department of Health, that there had been attempts over a number of years to organize a public health department in Midway, but for reasons that were not entirely clear these efforts never bore fruit. As the steering committee was going about its tasks, according to the timetable outlined above, there were new and revised stirrings regarding the establishment of a local health department.

Although the steering committee with which the mental health consultant had worked had not given a health department high priority, they had requested consultation and studied materials as described earlier. The mental health consultant also provided for the Division of Local Health Services in the State Health Department, on request, a list of core members of the steering committee, plus the names of other interested citizens who remained quite interested in the survey and other developments but who did not actually participate on the steering committee.

Consultants from the Division of Local Health Services and the mental health consultant exchanged information about visits to the community and attempted in every way to coordinate their work there. The Medical Association endorsed the establishment of a local health department. This action was independent of (and occurred after) their endorsement of the Family Guidance and Consultation Center. The County Commissioners, however, did not include the proposed health department in their budget for the next year.

Between November, 1961, and October, 1962, there were a number of discouraging developments which the chairman of the steering committee discussed with the consultant by phone, correspondence, and during occasional personal conferences. These included:

1. The passage of a bond issue for a very substantial sum to build a new county courthouse that distracted, temporarily at least, from funding of the Guidance Center.
2. The Chamber of Commerce, Civic Affairs Committee, which originally had initiated the request for consultation, had almost a complete turnover in committee membership. Consequently, the committee was providing little active support for the Guidance Center.
3. The Chamber of Commerce was giving attention to what it considered a more pressing need—attracting industry to the community—and was involved in a crash program to raise funds from businessmen. There had also been considerable turnover among the Chamber executives. In fact, both the director and his assistant resigned since the Chamber first requested consultation from the state's Division of Mental Health.
4. A new county judge was elected, plus several new city and county commissioners. Efforts to get funds from these sources had to be started again from scratch, as the newly elected officials had little or no understanding of the survey findings and recommendations. Furthermore, the city manager, with whom the steering committee had worked initially, resigned.

In the fall of 1962 the chairman asked the consultant to come to Midway for help in reappraising their goals, objectives, and community organization methods. The consultant, during the interval prior to this visit, had assured the chairman that in spite of the setbacks that they had encountered, he and his agency were still quite impressed with the work that had been done, the potentiality for development of services, and raising the necessary local funds.

One of the consultants from the Division of Local Health Services in the State Department of Health told the mental health consultant that several physicians and others with whom he had been working concerning the establishment of a health department had run up against many of the same kinds of problems as those confronting the steering committee concerned with establishment of the Guidance Center.

Merging Forces—Mental Health and Public Health

Early in the fall of 1962 the mental health consultant met as requested with the steering committee. They described the extensive educational campaign that had been carried out earlier in the year and which they thought had been quite effective. However, all were rather discouraged about the recent series of setbacks as outlined above. They felt the group from the Medical Association and others who were attempting to establish a health department had encountered many of the same difficulties.

The idea of the family guidance and consultation service being a part of the health department had been discussed in earlier meetings with the Medical Association and with the steering committee. At the time this was first considered, however, it seemed to the steering committee that there was much more community readiness for the guidance service than there was for the health department. Consequently, their efforts had been concentrated in this direction. So the two groups had really functioned almost entirely independently.

The consultant, in this meeting, raised as a possibility the joining of forces and combining of efforts of the several groups with the objective of establishing a health department that would include as an administrative part the Family Guidance and Consultation Center. The consultant also assured the group that he would discuss this with representatives from the Division of Local Health Services in the State Health Department so that if the local committees were interested, the State Health Department would consolidate and coordinate consultation efforts toward the combined services.

This proposal was received with some enthusiasm and seemed to provide the needed *remotivation* for the committee to resume activities. In fact, before the meeting was concluded, a number of details were worked out concerning combined organizational strategy. Plans were discussed for the steering committee to meet with the consultant from the Division of Local Health Services. He was scheduled to be in the city in a few months for a meeting with the new city manager.

The consultant from the Division of Local Health Services asked the mental health consultant to join him in the community in some of the conferences scheduled with the city manager, representatives from the Medical Association, and other groups. In these meetings budget details and technical questions concerning the various services and organizational strategies were discussed. The several groups indicated approval and enthusiasm for the joint service, and they proceeded to form organizational committees and subcommittees to proceed with establishing the combined services.

A part of the organizational strategy included a *town meeting,* to which the public was invited for questions and discussion about the proposed services. The director of the Division of Local Health Services and the mental health consultant attended this meeting, as requested, and served as resource persons to help answer questions from the audience concerning services, costs, staffing, etc. The overall response, questions, and discussion were of exceptionally high quality. Many from the audience enthusiastically offered their services to carry out needed organizational and educational work.

Crisis

The consultant and his sponsoring agency, Division of Mental Health, Texas State Department of Health, were convinced of the soundness of local planning, proposals for services, and priorities. They agreed to provide state financial assistance (in addition to providing ongoing consultative assistance) up to 50 percent (about $15,000 per year) of the total operating cost. This would provide staffing and services as outlined earlier in the section on committee recommendations.

State assistance depended on an increased appropriation. However, by April, 1963, it appeared extremely doubtful that additional funds would be available for new mental health services during the next biennium. Necessary "pump priming" funds for Midway and other communities for developing or extending their mental health services were not to become available until later.

The crisis was discussed with the chairman and the steering committee. In spite of their great disappointment and uncertainty about funding the service without state support, they were unanimous in their conviction and decision to move ahead in every possible way to establish the service. They asked the consultant for his continued assistance and suggestions as to how they might proceed. The consultant informed them that even though there was no assurance of state funding before the biennium beginning in September, 1965, he would make every effort to assist them further in their planning and fund recruitment efforts.

The consultant also informed them, after discussion with appropriate personnel, that the budget situation was not as critical within the Division of Local Health Services; and they planned to assist in establishing a local health department. The committee decided to proceed in the hope that needed financial help might be available from other sources to develop the mental health services as part of the health department, according to earlier plan.

Success

Both the mental health consultant and consultants from the Division of Local Health Services maintained active contact with the community through strategic committees, professional practitioners, and citizens who were interested in, but not necessarily a formal part of, the planning process. The Division of Local Health Services was able to provide sufficient funding, which when combined with local funds was enough to begin a modest public health service. The health department opened its doors for services in September, 1964.[7]

A psychiatrist with a strong interest in community mental health services was invited to the community for a series of interviews, including a joint one with the mental health consultant and the chairman of the steering committee. He subsequently established private practice in Midway later that year. He was also helpful in assisting the local health department director and the Board of Health with organizational details regarding the establishment of the Family Guidance and Consultation Center as an administrative unit of the health department. Later he became the medical director of the Family Guidance and Consultation Center.

The chairman of the earlier steering committee, the same man who chaired the first organizational meeting in 1960, was appointed as chairman of the Board of Health in 1964. He had provided outstanding and dedicated leadership throughout the organizational phases, first for the proposed Family Guidance and Consultation Center and later for the joint public health and mental health service. His appointment as chairman of the Board of Health assured a sound beginning for both services. The excellence of his work directly, and in concert with a corps of citizens with similar interests and dedication in developing the much needed public health and mental health services, cannot be overemphasized. His years of unremitting labor as chairman of the steering committee, and more recently as chairman of the Board of Health, won for him in 1966 a special award as "Man of the Year" by the Texas Association for Mental Health.

Although the Division of Mental Health was not able to provide funds in accordance with the timetable or amount as originally planned, it was able to provide a small amount of equipment for the Center and also some funds for the psychiatrist's services, both for help in planning and for selected direct patient services to adults and children beginning in April, 1965.

Also, the division, because of completion of a project in another area of the state earlier than had been anticipated, was able to transfer funds from this

---

[7] A few months later a combined child welfare unit and probation service began operations. Creation of these services came as a by-product of the steering committee's efforts. However, neither the committee nor the consultant was actually involved in the organization of the services or the decision to combine them.

project to Midway, allowing for recruitment of a full-time executive director (psychiatric social worker) for the family guidance and consultation service. Intensive recruitment, with active assistance and direction from the consultant, was carried out for more than a year before a qualified director was located. More than a dozen candidates were considered, and five were actually interviewed in the community before the director was selected in August, 1966. A psychometrist began part-time services early in 1967.

A second psychiatrist began part-time work with the Center in July, 1967. Currently efforts are underway to add a second full-time social worker. Recruitment is also underway for a part-time clinical psychologist. Long-range planning now in process includes extending a hand from Midway to neighboring communities to join forces in developing a comprehensive mental health and mental retardation center for a population area of 75,000 to 200,000 in accordance with both federal and state legislative and funding requirements.

The crisis described earlier was weathered because of intense local commitment and rally of forces to keep a dream and plan alive. Local funding from city, county, and private sources, together with a three-year promise of funds from a statewide voluntary foundation,[8] made launching of the service successful. Operations were assured until additional funding became available from the state to staff the service as originally planned, with a ratio of roughly 50% local funds and 50% state funds.

As Midway, along with neighboring communities, can successfully develop plans for comprehensive services, additional funding from local, state, and federal sources will be sought so as to implement a comprehensive mental health/mental retardation center program.

Summary and Questions

In Midway there were numerous obstacles, delays, and serious problems in establishing both public health and mental health services, but obstacles and problems were constructively met. The absence of state funds, along with local funding problems, delayed the establishment of the service. If funding could have been assured at an earlier stage, the writer is certain that the amount of

[8]The Hogg Foundation for Mental Health, University of Texas, Austin. Staff of the former Division of Mental Health, Texas State Department of Health and the Division of Community Services, Texas State Department of Mental Health and Mental Retardation, have enjoyed an excellent working relationship with the Hogg Foundation. The organizations have collaborated on helping with development of many innovative community projects over the years.

The complementary and supplementary interest and support provided by the Foundation were of critical importance in development of services in Midway, especially at this particular juncture. The reputation and prestige of the Foundation, statewide and nationally, were positive factors in influencing local sources of support when it became known that the Foundation was committing a modest amount of funds to help initiate the service.

organizational time and effort required to begin services could have been reduced by at least two-thirds.

If there had not been strong local involvement from the first in the survey of problems, planning of services, establishment of priorities, etc., the crisis in 1963 would not have been successfully weathered. If it had been a totally state-planned service, then the crisis presented by the inability to come up with state funding would have resulted in failure to develop a much needed service.

In summary, *key factors* in bringing the community to the present stage in organization, development, and operation of services include:

1. Effective problem definition.
2. The chairman's acceptance in the community and his competence, dedication, and persistence.
3. Acceptance of the consultant by community leaders and quality of the consultant-consultee relationship, including sustained support and encouragement through direct contacts, telephone conversations, and correspondence.
4. Local involvement in *all* phases of planning, education, interpretation, and organization of services.
5. Successful coordination of individual and agency efforts, both at local and state levels.
6. Establishing and refinement of boundaries and goals in a practical, dynamic way, consistent with the changing "mood and climate" of the organizational groups and the community at large.
7. Moving one step at a time with a flexible timetable and built-in assurance of some success with even the most time-limited and modest tasks and objectives.
8. Selection for the Center of competent administrative and service staff who have special personal and professional interests and skills in work with the smaller community.

The example (although it seems to the writer a good one from a community organization point of view) does raise some practical questions about the several roles of the community organization consultant, his sponsor, and the appropriateness of action and methods at certain steps along the way. Prominent among these are:

1. *Entry.* Since the original request was focused on juvenile delinquency and other youth problems, should the Division of Mental Health, which received the request, have directed the request to another organization? Entry by the mental health consultant seemed justified for several reasons. First, the interest in the pamphlet (published by the Division of Mental Health) prompted the request for help. Also, the request was discussed in advance with the State Youth Council responsible for providing consultation on probation services; and it was agreed that it was appropriate for the Division of Mental Health consultant to respond as outlined.
2. *State responsibility.* In the absence of a local planning body such as a community council, what should be the state's responsibility especially on the part of a public mental health agency for assisting with *problem definition,* measurement of the extent of the problem *(survey),* and consultation with citizen leaders toward development of needed services? Again, in this instance the entry and action described seemed justified. But a state mental health agency cannot respond to all such requests, at least not until the community has decided to focus specifically on development of mental health services.
3. *Which service(s).* In a community so lacking in "helping services" for troubled people, which one(s) should first be established? Any one of a dozen services would be helpful. When it

appears as if only one can be established, which one? And what is the consultant's responsibility for helping citizen and professional leaders for arriving at a decision? In this instance these decisions were made by the local committee with the help of expert information provided both by the mental health (community organization) consultant and other specialized consultants brought in from related fields.

4. *Role of the consultant.* In the absence of appropriate local resources and limited state resources that might assist communities with needed health and welfare surveys, planning, training, etc., what should the role of the mental health consultant be in such a situation? From the summary presented, several roles—coordinator, survey assistant, teacher-trainer, recruitment specialist—have been identified. Even though every effort was made within the varied roles to assure the community freedom of choice, there is always danger of some "contamination" because of the particular field that the consultant represents.

5. *Ongoing consultation responsibility.* What ongoing responsibility should the consultant have, if any? What are the advantages and disadvantages of having the consultant who assisted during the organizational phases continue after the service begins operations? In this example the same consultant continued, both in providing consultation to the staff of the Family Guidance and Consultation Center regarding program, funding, community relationships, etc., and also in working with staff and citizen leaders in surrounding communities regarding development of comprehensive mental health/mental retardation services on a regional basis. This seemed to be the most practical solution to providing needed ongoing consultative services. There are advantages, however, in bringing in fresh consultation and new perspective when such are available, and the consultant has at strategic times helped the community to utilize specialized consultants from other fields for a variety of planning and service operations.

Large metropolitan areas or states with an abundance and variety of consultative and planning resources would no doubt undertake problem-solving and organization, as outlined in this example, in other ways. However, for those involved in planning efforts, especially in underdeveloped regions, the example and concluding questions should have discussion value not only for community organization consultants but in varied formal and inservice training efforts in mental health, mental retardation, public health, and related fields.

The following reference seems particularly relevant to the example and process described:

"The professional workers involved have the clear assignment to help the community develop toward its highest level of accomplishment. The lay citizens involved have the final responsibility for determining the goal, the plan, and the timing, manner, and level of achievement. Finally, community destiny lies in citizen participation and authority. And competent professional assistance to citizens can make the community decisions toward its destiny wiser and firmer as a foundation for still higher levels of community development. It can make the participating citizens better able to solve future community problems (Stumpf, 1962)."

References

McNeil, C. F. Community organization for social welfare. In R. H. Kurtz (Ed.), *Social Work Year Book, 1954.* (12th issue.) New York: NASW, 1954. Pp. 121–122.

Murphy, C. G. Community organization for social welfare. In R. H. Kurtz (Ed.), *Social Work Year Book, 1957.* (13th issue.) New York: NASW, 1957. P. 179.

Rieman, D. W. Group mental health consultation with public health nurses. In L. Rapoport (Ed.), *Consultation in social work practice.* New York: NASW, 1963. Pp. 85–86.

Stern, E. M. *Talk is cheaper.* Austin: Texas State Department of Health, Division of Mental Health, 1959.

Stumpf, J. Roles and relationships of participants. In R. L. Warren (Ed.), *Community development and social work practice.* New York: NASW, 1962. P. 30.

Texas State Department of Health, Division of Mental Health. *Guide to action for development of community mental health services with survey guides.* Austin, 1963.

Part II

Programs with a
Mental Health Service Orientation

One of the major ways of intervening within the field of community mental health is to evaluate, coordinate and, if necessary, restructure the mental health services within a community. Although some social action may take place and some overall organizational changes occur, the primary focus is in developing those services traditionally seen as clinical mental health services. These have been identified in recent Federal legislation (Community Mental Health Centers Act Title II, 1963, 88–164) as outpatient services, inpatient services, emergency services, education and consultation services, pre-care and after-care services, partial hospitalization, research and evaluation, diagnostic services, rehabilitation, and training.

But good clinical services are not just a collection of clinical activities. The legislation specifies that the services must be characterized by continuity of care, coordination, and comprehensiveness.

Despite the clear specifications within the law, there is wide latitude for establishing services most appropriate for a given area, as well as evolving new ways of delivering services or increasing the effectiveness of current operations. One such area, relatively new as a mental health service, is consultation service to institutions such as schools, hospitals, or other agencies whose functioning, although often not directly related to mental health, has wide mental health implications.

This section attempts to show the wide variety of ways mental health services have been developed to meet various needs and purposes. It covers the problems of developing services for a rural population as well as those encountered in urban areas. It shows two types of approaches to services in urban areas: one based in an urban general hospital, and the other neighborhood-based but affiliated with the general hospital. It also presents the issues in developing appropriate services within the schools as an example of what is encountered in consultative work with agencies.

All the chapters in this section are characterized basically by an elaboration and expansion of the clinical model in the development of mental health services. They differ from the chapters in the previous section where primary emphasis was placed upon local community action and community participation in the evolution, organization, development, and implementation of programs.

Chapter 4
The Development of an Urban Comprehensive Community Mental Health Program

Horace G. Whittington

Although there is considerable flexibility in the implementation of programs under the recently enacted mental health legislation, the chief focus is based on the patient-oriented treatment and rehabilitation approach of medicine. In this chapter, Dr. Whittington has translated the services listed in the mental health legislation into his hospital-based urban community mental health program. He sets the framework for his program when he says, "There is no substitute for good clinical psychiatry." However, two features stand out. Clinical psychiatry now incorporates new areas, such as home visits, indigenous workers, and family approaches, as part of the treatment program. Second, considerable emphasis is placed upon work with community "caretakers" through the use of collaboration, consultation, and participation in inservice training programs.

Chapter 4

The Development of an Urban Comprehensive Community Mental Health Program

Horace G. Whittington

Brave new worlds are made of the shattered dreams of yesteryear. Fragments of unfilled promises and frustrated omnipotence, like bits of broken crystal, make a dazzling mosaic of the familiar jumbled together in new combinations—a thousand facets that glitter brightly under the light of rekindled idealism.

The comprehensive community mental health center, put together from the wreckage of past failures in psychiatry, stands as a monument to American pragmatism. A hodgepodge of compromise and simplistic conceptualization, of anglophilia and Jeffersonian ruralism, of therapeutic optimism and nihilism, its hybrid vigor is impressive (Kennedy, 1964).

The comprehensive community mental health center is a dream that has become our national policy, with which our national resolve and purpose are identified. This is the first time that the disparate and competitive antecedents of psychiatry have congealed into an integrated, internally consistent framework of belief and practice. The future of psychiatry rides—on the back of this national committee-assembled, far-from-perfect social innovation—toward the 21st century in the midst of currents dedicated to the completion of the American social revolution.

And, dependent as the American community is on Federal financing to bring this dream to reality, no community mental health program can develop without reference to national policy; no community mental health program can exist in a vacuum.

As the state director of community mental health services in Kansas and of the state planning projects in mental health and mental retardation, the author became increasingly aware that most of psychiatry's "bets" were being placed on the national model of the comprehensive community mental health center (Whittington, 1966). Awareness of the powerful resistance of conservative, vested interests in psychiatry was likewise inescapable. The inadequate preparation of all mental health disciplines to implement the comprehensive commu-

65

nity mental health concept was also too evident. And yet the bets were laid, the wheel was turning.

The author then decided to abandon his secure position as a state-level administrator not responsible for the direct operation of a clinical program and to devote himself to the day-by-day, hard, and often dirty, business of trying to convert imperfect dreams into the tangible reality of a metropolitan comprehensive community mental health program. He became Director of Psychiatry for the Denver (Colorado) Department of Health and Hospitals in September, 1965, responsible for mental health services for the 540,000 citizens of Denver County.

The five-county metropolitan area of Denver (with a population of over one million) lies in a semi-arid plain at the eastern base of the Rocky Mountains. The city is a major distribution and transportation hub for a vast but sparsely populated area. The largest ethnic minority group is made up of Spanish Americans; next in size is the Negro population. Denver is a forward-looking city; workable solutions to its physical and social problems have been, and are, well planned and implemented. The granting of federal Model Cities funds is a comment on Denver's continual search for improvement.

There are many stories that could be told about the development of comprehensive community mental health services in the city and county of Denver. Some are sad; some humorous. Each is filled with the same sense of urgency and poignant reality that all involved in the civil upheaval of the 1960's—whether in mental health, civil rights, or war on poverty—experience. Many of these encounters are so prototypical that they have little new to teach or demonstrate. The plight of the cities in finances, education, maintenance of civil order, social betterment, and civilian morale applies to Denver as to all urban complexes.

This discussion, therefore, concentrates on two particular aspects of problems encountered in developing a comprehensive community mental health program in Denver County:

1. How does a general hospital-based psychiatric department, held in low esteem by lay citizens and professionals alike, and isolated from the community, better its position?
2. How are the 200,000 population catchment areas, required by federal community mental health program regulations, to be defined in a larger populated, multiple-agency, urban setting?

The Program

In the early 1960's the situation of Denver General Hospital (operated by the Department of Health and Hospitals) was similar in many ways to that of other municipal general hospitals. Housed in an ancient facility, starved for funds, understaffed, strangled by a coterie of "old timers" who had outlasted successive generations of idealistic young professionals, vulnerable to political manipulation, lodged at the bottom of the professional hierarchy, it limped along from year to year serving increasing numbers of patients with fixed resources. Denver General Hospital's one tie to excellence, its affiliation with the University of Colorado Medical School, had been severed in a town-gown struggle which was also influenced by party politics.

By 1965 the situation had begun to change markedly. Optimism was in the air, and years of inertia were giving way to a phase of unparalleled growth. Many factors had contributed to this change:

In the city election of 1962, improvement of Denver General Hospital was a campaign issue of the elected candidate.

In 1964 a series of bond issues was proposed. The bond issue for constructing a new Denver General Hospital passed by a larger plurality than any of the other issues. This message was not lost on the politicians of Denver.

The mayor appointed an unusually capable administrator as Deputy Manager of Health and Hospitals to encourage the upgrading of Denver General Hospital and its eventual re-affiliation with the University of Colorado Medical School.

A young and imaginative Director of Public Health was appointed by the mayor and given encouragement to develop a network of comprehensive health care services in low-income neighborhoods of Denver.

A happy congruence of new federal aid programs made possible a massive influx of new money to Denver. Funds were obtained from the Office of Economic Opportunity (for the neighborhood health program), the Children's Bureau (for neighborhood maternal and infant care and children and youth health programs), and, later, the National Institute of Mental Health (for constructing and staffing the comprehensive community mental health center), and several other sources.

In 1966 an energetic and idealistic physician was appointed Manager of Health and Hospitals by the mayor; his leadership has been vigorous and creative.

It was in the midst of this sequence of events that the author came to Denver. He chose Denver, after visiting several cities, because he believed conditions were right to allow and support an innovative community mental health program. The successes of Denver's mental health program today are not so much the result of extraordinary ability; rather, they are a comment on the importance of discerning social readiness for change.

This "social readiness for change" can be gauged by several criteria. In addition to those factors that affected primarily the Department of Health and Hospitals and Denver General Hospital, the author became aware of the "climate" of the community that would foster a sound mental health program—a steady rate of economic growth, higher than national averages of education and income, a solid two-party political system, vigorous intellectual and professional communities, pluralism and division of power among caregiving systems, community support for human betterment programs, reasonably dependable political leadership, commitment to human services, and so on.

Immediate challenges to the new programs of the Department of Health and Hospitals and to the improvement of Denver General Hospital came—not from the "man on the street" or the informed influential layman—but from the allied caregiving professions and agencies in Denver. Three major sources of resistance to the new developments were identified:

The local medical society viewed the reformation of the "charity hospital" with alarm. The development of neighborhood health centers and stations, to extend quality medical care into impoverished neighborhoods, was particularly opposed. Bitterness and alienation of the Department of Health and Hospitals' medical staff from organized medicine in Denver developed.

The state-level hospital facilities planning committee opposed the construction of a new Denver General Hospital. The committee felt that Denver had sufficient hospital beds and maintained that Medicare would make city hospitals obsolete.

Voluntary and private agencies in Denver were also alarmed by the rapid upsurge of public services. Competition for staff, prestige, and funds fueled their sense of threat. Rather than active opposition, however, agency representatives pointed out the impermanence of federal funding ("soft money") and predicted the downfall of expanded neighborhood health services.

The consensus of administrators and directors of service of the Department of Health and Hospitals was that social progress always arouses anxiety and resistance. This problem was dealt with matter-of-factly by trying to state our agency's goals clearly, by demonstrating our resolve and our willingness to work jointly with other community agencies and professional organizations, and by moving ahead deliberately to do what we believed was necessary. No energy was spent on the belief that total community consensus could or should be reached, nor on attempts to cajole, seduce, or bribe resistant groups.

As an integrated part of the Department of Health and Hospitals, the Division of Psychiatric Services shared some of the stigma and received some of the benefits of the program expansion. The mental health program itself, however, never became a public target. Neither was the legitimacy of our intention to develop a comprehensive community mental health program ever questioned.

The District Branch of the American Psychiatric Association was most supportive, as were the state and local chapters of the American Psychological Association and the National Association of Social Workers. The state mental health authority and the Department of Psychiatry at the University of Colorado Medical School likewise lent full support.

Broad community recognition of the need for expanded public psychiatric services, the educational efforts of the Denver Association for Mental Health, and the community's social consciousness and responsible commitment to human betterment can also be given credit for endorsing the development of comprehensive mental health services in Denver.

Significant problems did develop (and to a lesser degree have persisted) in our relationship with Fort Logan Mental Health Center, the state hospital that serves Denver, located at the southwestern border of the community. Conflicts have centered around differences in treatment philosophies and disagreement about the role of the state hospital in this phase of psychiatric development. Monthly formal interagency meetings and numerous informal and ad hoc conferences have helped resolve some of these differences, and have set the stage for continuing conflict resolution. A separate paper will discuss our difficulties and attempts to resolve them in further detail.

All in all, initiation of the comprehensive community mental health program by the Department of Health and Hospitals met no genuine resistance. With support from city administrators, initial changes were made, and staff increases begun. The recommendations of Colorado's mental health planning project were used in assigning priorities for the development of new mental health services and programs. Applications for community mental health center staffing and construction grants were prepared and submitted to the National Institute of Mental Health (Bindman & Kleganoff, 1959; Goldston, 1965; Group for the Advancement of Psychiatry, 1964; State Mental Health Planning Committee, 1965).

We had begun.

It soon became clear that a community mental health program has a number of "constituencies," each of which has different expectations and different needs, and each of which must be met and served. The constituencies we identified primarily as different types of consumer groups. Their short-term and long-range needs and expectations became apparent as we set about planning the services they requested. The subsequent discussion is centered on five of the constituencies we identified and with whom we are working: the patients and their families, other community caregiving agencies and professionals, community social control and law enforcement agencies, other service divisions of the Department of Health and Hospitals, and the "man on the street."

The *patients* and their *families* wanted relief from troubling feelings and/or behaviors. We instituted a number of modifications to gain the support of this constituency (American Public Health Association, 1962; Bellak & Small, 1965; Riessman, Cohen & Pearl, 1964; Williams, 1962):

1. Prompt initial appointments are insured in each of five generic ("general practice") mental health teams. Specified hours each week are held open by one or more members of the generic teams. During this time new patients (both children and adults) are seen for evaluation. In no instance does a patient wait more than one or two days for his evaluation interview; there is no waiting list.

2. Expanded psychiatric emergency services was a top priority recommendation of the state mental health planning project. Our application for federal staffing funds reflected this studied need, and with the awarding of federal funds we were able to employ a team of psychologist-coordinator and four psychiatric nurses to work in the emergency room of Denver General Hospital. Coverage is now provided 16 hours each working day, and 8 hours on the two weekend days. With the assistance of an additional staffing grant, we plan to expand coverage to 24 hours within the year. The team also maintains a telephone suicide prevention service around the clock; medical direction is provided by the director of psychiatric consultation.

3. Employment of indigenous nonprofessionals to reach out to patients is one of the many strong points of the neighborhood health program of the Department of Health and Hospitals. Two of the five generic mental health teams are assigned to the two Neighborhood Health Centers (established

by the Department with grant assistance from the Office of Economic Opportunity) that provide comprehensive health care services to low-income families in Denver. Indigenous "neighborhood aides" are selected and given pre-service training by the local Community Action Project and the Department of Health and Hospitals; they are assigned to all clinical and service areas of the Centers and given needed inservice training by the clinicians and personnel with whom they work. The eight aides working with the two mental health teams perform needed clerical duties, follow missed appointments, conduct activity and other social groups for patients, serve as translators when necessary, assist families with practical problems and emotional resistance to coming to the Center, counsel patients' families, and in general help patients understand the need for and methods of psychiatric treatment.

4. Utilization of visiting nurse service to take treatment services into the homes of patients had been a relatively unused resource by the Division of Psychiatric Services before the initiation of comprehensive community mental health services. Now visiting nurse service receives referrals for many psychiatric patients. Visiting nurses counsel families of patients in 24-hour, day care, or outpatient treatment; they help families prepare for a patient's return home after hospitalization, and they provide follow-up and needed aftercare services following treatment. They conduct needed home evaluation visits, counsel families of children in treatment, check medications the patient is taking, follow victims of sexual assault and suicide attempts who come to the hospital emergency room, help patients and families follow medical and psychiatric recommendations, provide emotional support, and act as a vital casefinding and referral link in our comprehensive program.

5. Emphasis on services to family units, a long-standing but little used finding of psychiatric research, was put into practice in our comprehensive community mental health program. Members of the specialized child psychiatry team were reassigned to the generic teams; the generic teams were charged with responsibility for assuming a *family* orientation to treatment. Not only families of children but, whenever possible, families of *all* patients are offered counseling and encouraged to participate in treatment plans of the generic teams. Formal family therapy is also provided by the generic teams when needed.

6. Increased continuity of care is insured by the five generic teams. Unless a patient is seen in the emergency room or in consultation on another ward of the hospital, his first contact is with a member of the generic team that serves the geographic area of Denver where he lives. This team member conducts the first interview, continues to see the patient in treatment, and will again treat the patient if he relapses after termination. If the patient needs 24-hour or day hospitalization, a member of the area generic team attends hospital staff conferences for treatment and discharge planning; he is also a co-therapist in small group therapy sessions for patients hospitalized from his team's service area of Denver. Referral to this area generic team is made automatically, before discharge from hospital treatment, so continuing outpatient treatment can be provided as long as necessary.

7. Elimination of delays and complicated procedures is also a responsibility of the generic mental health team. Appointments for evaluation are given on the strength of a single phone call. Referring agencies are requested to send the team a written case summary before the initial appointment if possible, although this is not mandatory. Neither is it necessary for the patient himself to call for the appointment, if the referring agency gives the team verbal assurance of the patient's consent and willingness to keep the appointment. Every patient of Denver General Hospital must have a hospital identification plate. New patients, however, who have not yet obtained a plate are seen for evaluation and asked to get a plate from the hospital admissions office before the next appointment.

8. Increased availability of care was accomplished through the geographic decentralization of the five generic teams. At present three of the teams have moved out of the hospital into small clinic facilities central to the catchment areas they serve. A fourth team will move from the hospital in early 1968. The fifth team, which serves the central city area surrounding Denver General Hospital, will remain in the hospital.

9. Treatment modalities were expanded so that treatment could be individually selected to meet the needs of each patient. A wide variety of treatment—individual, group, or family psychotherapy;

socialization and activity group experiences; day care or 24-hour hospital treatment; vocational rehabilitation counseling; psychoeducational treatment for children; psychodrama; and other modalities—are provided for patients according to their needs. We have no standard "prepackaged plan" of treatment to which patients must accommodate themselves.

We believe that services that adequately and flexibly meet the needs of the patient constituency are the key factor in obtaining and maintaining support for the community mental health program. Contrary to what clinicians sometimes say and feel, grateful patients *do* exist. And relatives and friends and other care-giving agencies *do* listen to what they say.

There is no substitute for the practice of good clinical psychiatry.

Other caregiving agencies in the community are another constituency, or consumer group, for the services of the comprehensive community mental health program. Our strategy in the beginning was to meet their perceived needs, as quickly and well as possible, so that we could learn from each other our mutual needs, expectations, and misperceptions. Only after this "groundwork" of understanding and working together was laid did we attempt to refocus their expectations into more realistic channels and to develop with them mutually collaborative working relationships. Several changes were instituted in our program to give the caregiving agencies easy and immediate access to our services (Caplan, 1964). These changes not only met the perceived needs of the agencies, they also gave the Division of Psychiatric Services the advantage of "social credit" with the other agencies so that genuine collaboration could evolve naturally.

Our psychiatric emergency services were greatly expanded. The need for these services was detailed by the Denver committee of the Colorado mental health planning project; the recommendation for expanding emergency services received top priority in the committee's final report. The committee's study showed that psychiatric emergency services were the most keenly perceived need of all caregiving agencies in the city.

Referrals from other caregiving agencies were encouraged. Before the comprehensive program was instituted, referrals for outpatient treatment were accepted only when the patient called for an appointment. This requirement was abolished, and other agencies were allowed to make appointments for their clients when it was desirable.

Regular consultation was offered the Denver Department of Welfare and the Visiting Nurse Service of the Department of Health and Hospitals. This offer was accepted eagerly, and plans were instituted with the two agencies. Consultation began with the Family Services Division of the Welfare Department; two-member teams of the psychiatric staff (of all disciplines) met each month with several casework units. This program is now entering its third year. In addition to the units in the Family Services Division (which includes Aid to Dependent Children, the Title V Program, and several student units), consultation is provided regularly to the Aged and Medical Services Division and to Child Welfare as needed. About 200 visiting nurses are assigned to geographic service areas, much the same as the catchment areas of the generic mental health teams. Regular monthly consultation to the visiting nurses working in their areas was begun by the generic teams. The format of this consultation continues—a member or members of the team (of any discipline) meets each month with the field visiting nurses in the service area.

Leaflets and other handout materials were developed to provide other agencies with needed information about our services as they expanded. Preservice training about our services and ways of utilizing them was begun for new visiting nurses, new caseworkers of the Welfare Department, and new employees of other community agencies.

Collaborative efforts to share personnel were proposed to the visiting nurse service, the Denver Public Schools, and Child Welfare. As a result, the visiting nurse consultant on alcoholism works as a staff member on our service; and the mental health consultant works closely with us in a planning and collaborative capacity. A special education teacher from the public schools works full time in the psychiatric day school for emotionally disturbed and perceptually handicapped children. Planning with Child Welfare for joint responsibility for a short-term residential treatment facility for children continues.

Information was requested from other caregiving agencies whenever a case evaluation was begun. This had not been done in the past, with the result that referring agencies perceived the Division of Psychiatric Services as feeling that their work and knowledge of the patient were not important enough for our consideration. Now, in addition to recognizing the value of the other agency's work with the patient, our request for the case summary also quickly provides our staff with necessary patient information that might have been learned only after several interviews, or that the patient might not have told us at all.

We are convinced that this pattern of working with other caregiving agencies in the community is a crucial one for the comprehensive mental health program. Perceived needs must be met with a helpful response before confidence and new types of interagency relationships can be evolved.

A variety of *social control agencies*—police, courts, jails, probation and parole officers—were clearly a large consumer group for the services of the comprehensive community mental health center in Denver. We accordingly expanded our services in several ways:

1. At the request of the Denver Association for Mental Health, we helped plan and conduct a two-day seminar on mental health for district court probation officers. Lectures and discussions centered on understanding human behavior, suicidal and other deviant behavior, and the services available in our comprehensive program. Although this was a relatively short-term learning experience for the probation officers, we feel the seminar has had a long-term effect in helping the officers understand their probationers and utilize our services effectively.

2. The director of the Denver Police Training Academy welcomed our request to participate in the training of recruit policemen. After a series of planning conferences involving both our staff and police academy staff, we began with a one-hour lecture and discussion session of normal and maladaptive behavior and the policeman's responsibilities in Denver's community mental health program. Our participation in the 11-week training session has subsequently been increased to two hours; police classes came to the hospital to see our emergency, hospital, and outpatient services, and their academic training is increasingly centered on more discussion than lectures. Police trainees evaluate each training session we conduct, and we endeavor to incorporate their suggestions into each approaching new session. At the last joint planning-evaluation meeting of psychiatric and police training staff, we agreed that our training session should be extended further to adequately prepare the policeman for understanding and handling the mentally ill.

3. The Denver County Court, with assistance of a Federal Aid to Law Enforcement Agencies grant, established a psychiatric screening clinic and began a counseling program utilizing volunteer "probation officers." A member of our staff directs the diagnostic clinic and provides consultation to the volunteer counselors.

4. Regular consultation is provided to the probation officers of the district court, at the request of the probation department.

5. Consultation is provided, on request, to the police physician. In addition to his medical duties at the city jail, he directs the holding unit operated jointly by the Department of Safety and Excise and the Department of Health and Hospitals, located on the grounds of Denver General Hospital. Many patients detained in the holding unit for legal-medical reasons have psychiatric illnesses, and are a frequent focus of consultation.

Other *service divisions* of the Department of Health and Hospitals also demanded additional psychiatric assistance. Several responses to their expressed needs were made:

Our psychiatric liaison service, providing consultation for inpatients and outpatients of other wards and clinics of Denver General Hospital, was greatly enhanced by the addition of a full-time psychiatrist to our staff, designated with total responsibility for this consultive work. The director of psychiatric consultation is also responsible for the psychiatric training of interns and residents in the hospital; in addition to consulting with house officers about management and treatment planning for specific cases, he provides a variety of formal and informal learning opportunities. Many of the general interns and nonpsychiatric residents at Denver General Hospital begin practicing in the Rocky Mountain area; we feel that our consultation has a far-reaching effect in helping new physicians understand the mental health implications of any medical practice.

A specialized outpatient treatment program for alcoholics was begun, and the treatment team we recruited was augmented by the reassignment of the visiting nurse service consultant on alcoholism to our staff. This specialized program has operated for more than a year, with patients referred from all service divisions of the Department of Health and Hospitals as well as from other community caregiving agencies. The city of Denver is now planning to open a detoxification unit for alcoholics. When that service begins, members of our treatment team will be reassigned to the generic teams so that comprehensive psychiatric services for alcoholics and their families can be provided at the neighborhood level.

When the two Neighborhood Health Centers of the Department of Health and Hospitals were in the planning stages, we were closely involved in planning the inclusion of psychiatric services in the designated low-income neighborhoods. Two generic mental health teams were recruited and assigned to work in the Neighborhood Health Centers operated by the Public Health Division of the Department of Health and Hospitals.

Other elements of the neighborhood health program—maternal and infant care centers, several neighborhood health stations—were being planned and developed in conjunction with the two comprehensive Neighborhood Health Centers. Many of these additional neighborhood facilities are now operating, and regular psychiatric consultation to the staff of these facilities supplements the other health services available.

At the request of staff of the tuberculosis service at Denver General Hospital, we provided training and assistance in beginning a "therapeutic community," the treatment approach utilized on the psychiatric hospital service.

We are continuing efforts to make therapeutic and consultive services readily available to all other divisions of the Department of Health and Hospitals. Frequent communications interpret new program developments and plans for operating the comprehensive community mental health center within the general hospital and our willingness to plan cooperatively with other divisions for providing health services in Denver.

The *citizens* of Denver, as is true in most urban settings, are difficult to reach directly. They are bombarded with messages and pleas for support, and they have developed a selective inattention to shield themselves from sensory overload. Their attitudes are quite different from those of people living in rural and small communities; a significant number of those people *can* be approached directly. They are willing to lend their support and to participate responsibly in community action efforts. Our efforts to involve Denver citizens in our program have been considerable, but of questionable utility:

Psychiatric staff members are encouraged to participate in civic activities, and do—on committees of the Denver Planning Board, the Denver Urban Renewal Authority, the Denver and Metropolitan Mental Health Associations, professional organizations, school advisory committees, and so forth.

Staff members are encouraged to speak in public; the Department of Health and Hospitals participates in activities of the speakers bureau of the Denver Adult Education Council.

Interested citizens and members of related organizations (such as the mental health association) are encouraged to work on generic teams and the hospital service as volunteers.

Each of the generic and specialized teams are developing citizen advisory boards representative of the neighborhoods served.

Our overall strategy in establishing our comprehensive community mental health program has been consistent. We have demonstrated our willingness to realign our thinking and practice to be congruent with the expectations of our constituent groups. We avoid competition. We stress interdependency with other segments of the caregiving community. And we have established a "social credit account" by accommodating other agencies and professionals, upon which we can draw to develop more meaningful and stable collaborative relationships.

Does it work?
The immediate results are not inconsiderable:

Two years ago 45 patients were referred to the Visiting Nurse Service each month. In October, 1967 visiting nurses provided home treatment services to 399 psychiatric patients; they made a total of 867 visits.

The Denver Department of Welfare has extended its assistance repeatedly to help us meet the needs of our patients.

The Denver Public Schools and the Visiting Nurse Service contribute full-time personnel to our staff.

Patients are better prepared for referral to the Division of Psychiatric Services by other caregiving agencies.

And we anticipate that the long-range yield will be even greater. By emphasizing services to meet expressed needs, mutual definition of superordinate goals, and open communication, we have built—and are continuing to build—a matrix of interdependent relationships with vital community agencies in our urban setting. The continued growth and development of our program is to their advantage.

We have *not* reached the "man in the street." For the most part, he is totally indifferent to our very existence. In spite of our relative success in working with other caregiving constituencies, we are still viewed with distrust by organized medicine and with ambivalence by some psychiatrists. We hope to remedy this basic weakness in our community stance by involving almost 200 influential citizens and opinion setters—physicians, judges, school personnel, the clergy, city councilmen, and others—on citizen advisory boards being developed by generic and specialty teams.

Concerted effort toward developing advisory councils began in September, 1967, when a two-day seminar on community organization was conducted for selected liaison representatives of each team, who were designated with primary responsibility for forming their team's advisory council. The advisory councils will ideally be composed of about 15 opinion setters and professional group representatives within the geographic service areas (of the generic teams) or the subspecialty area of psychiatry (of the specialized psychiatric teams, such as the hospital services team). The purpose of the councils is to help elicit community support, to keep the team informed of community sentiment and related programs in the area, to assess mental health needs of the community served and assist in the development of new services or programs, and to develop educational and informational programs for citizens in the area. At present, two teams have organized citizen advisory councils, and other teams are moving ahead rapidly to develop advisory groups. In addition to affording meaningful involvement in our program to influential Denver citizens, we believe the advisory councils will provide a sensitive communications link between our staff and the publics we serve—a link that is vital to the responsive community mental health program.

Catchment Areas

Brave new worlds are customarily wreathed in oversimplifications, heralding perfection, and soon falling prey to the inexorable pressures of reality.

The concept of the geographic catchment area "of no less than 75,000 or more than 200,000" promised to bring order out of chaos, and neatness out of disarray. It has proved to have limited relevance to 20th-century urban life. The basic flaw in this concept is that urban communities are not functionally organized along neatly defined geographic boundaries. Only the public school system, whose foundation is now being shaken by the civil rights crisis, hews to the geographic model. Urban planning groups are increasingly recognizing that the catchment area concept is an unworkable basis for comprehensive planning and are abandoning it.

This is particularly true in current reappraisals of the educational system, which is now recognizing that the geographic model has, in reality, fostered de facto segregation. The Federal Housing Authority's concept of "neighborhood" has left us a legacy of dull, stiflingly homogeneous and multiply segregated suburban communities. The Society and City Subcommittee of the Denver Planning Board, of which the author is a member, has discovered, both from its own studies and from the publications of other groups concerned with future developments of urban living, that the geographic model is an inadequate foundation for institutions and agencies of human betterment.

The simple reality is this. ǀThe life spaces of the housewife and young child ǝre the only ones organized along geographic lines. The adolescent, the adult man, and the employed woman have life spaces that are not at all geographically defined. The higher the adult is on the educational and economic continuum, the less is his phenomenal world defined by a geographic neighborhood. His profession, his employment setting, his civic interest, and his professional organizations are more salient in defining his life space than the area surrounding his home. Services organized for a geographic neighborhood can be expected to serve housewives and children well; adults and young adults whose vocational and social orientations are away from the home will not be reached. The statistics of mental health agencies substantiate that this is exactly what happens.

It is ironic that, at this late date, the mental health subculture has based its new concept on the geographic catchment area.

It is equally unfortunate that the Federal guidelines for comprehensive community mental health programs do not recognize the complexities of urban planning, the slowness of genuine change, the overwhelming intricacies of reciprocal forces in urban society. The price we pay years from now for the present compulsive pleasure of drawing neat catchment area boundaries on maps may be enormous. Heightened interagency conflict, limited growth potential for vigorous and effective agencies that do not receive Federal community mental health funds, simplistic and mechanistic thinking, further fragmented authority and responsibility—any or all of these "prices" might be paid for the boundaries communities must define to satisfy distant planners and administrators.

Yet draw them we must. Without Federal construction and staffing assistance, the mental health program director in an urban setting stands little chance of mounting an effective program. The game must be played.

The Denver Department of Health and Hospitals is charged with responsibility, by the city charter, for "the physical and mental health of the people" of Denver. There are 540,000 people living in the city and county.

To obtain NIMH construction and staffing assistance, we had to choose 200,000 people out of that population, in a geographically contiguous area, and bestow upon them additional services denied the other 340,000 citizens.

With a local mandate of responsibility for *all* citizens and a Federal restriction on services for only *part* of those citizens, we had reached a potential impasse. Fortunately the Mental Health Program Director of the Public Health Service Regional Office in Denver gave us his active support and assistance. He called a meeting of the state mental health authority, the author, and representatives of all other mental health agencies that would be directly or indirectly affected by city-wide planning for comprehensive community mental health services. There were several purposes for the meeting—to allow agencies to plan for shared responsibility, to define individual agency goals, to share information and plans, and to involve the private sector in planning and providing public comprehensive services for the city.

Out of this initial meeting grew an ad hoc committee, chaired by the chairman of the Department of Psychiatry of the University of Colorado Medical School. A series of meetings over the ensuing months led to several decisions and plans:

1. A private psychiatric hospital will not participate in the city-wide public community mental health program.

2. An outpatient child guidance clinic will remain a specialized treatment facility.

3. The psychiatric department of a hospital for children already serves a large, several-state region; they will retain this identity and not develop comprehensive services for a small in-city catchment area.

4. The Department of Psychiatry at the University of Colorado Medical School will develop comprehensive services for about 100,000 persons in northeast Denver.

5. A private, church-operated psychiatric hospital will develop public comprehensive services for about 100,000 people in southeast Denver.

6. Cooperative relationships between mental health centers in the suburban Denver counties and Fort Logan Mental Health Center were developed to insure continuity and comprehensiveness of care for patients from those counties requiring inpatient or partial hospital treatment.

7. A cooperative undertaking of the Department of Health and Hospitals and Fort Logan Mental Health Center will provide comprehensive community mental health services in southwest Denver. Negotiations are underway to decentralize our southwest Denver generic team; inpatient services will be provided by Fort Logan, with free movement of patients and clinical records insured. The generic teams will initially be located in temporary facilities; eventually the team will be located in office facilities in the new Southwest Denver Community Center, now being planned.

8. Comprehensive community mental health services in northwest Denver will continue to be provided by the Department of Health and Hospitals.

Several major problems remain to be solved before the comprehensive mental health program in urban Denver can be considered adequate:

a. Jurisdictional fragmentation between state and city governments, urban and suburban counties, public and private sectors, medical and nonmedical agencies, is still enormous.

b. Services for alcoholics and their families are meager. Active planning to develop a spectrum of needed services is now being conducted jointly by involved city agencies.

c. Psychiatric facilities for children and adolescents are scanty. Planning in this area, at either a state or local level, has scarcely begun.

d. There are no local services for the drug addict or abuser.

e. There are no local services for the disorder offender. State resources are limited.

f. The transition of patients from state hospitals to the community is characterized by treatment discontinuity.

g. Psychiatric rehabilitation services, including halfway houses and sheltered workshops (both short-term and terminal) are in extremely short supply.

h. Manpower resources, both quantitatively and qualitatively, are inadequate in all disciplines. Psychiatrists trained in community mental health practice are most scarce.

i. Our knowledge about the descriptive aspects of psychiatric illnesses and our theories about causation are not matched by our demonstrated treatment capacity.

j. Our efforts are largely absorbed in tertiary prevention. Secondary prevention receives some attention, but primary prevention still lies in the realm of good intentions.

Yet progress has occurred in Denver these last two years.

Dorothea Dix's pessimism about the community's ability and willingness to care for its mentally ill citizens has proved wrong, at least in part. The author has found from his own experience, however, that the translation of idealistic schemes into practical, everyday reality is difficult and fraught with adversity. Social progress comes slowly because it is damned hard work.

That progress comes at all to community mental health is a tribute to the vision of the Joint Commission on Mental Illness and Health (1961), the vigorous if sometimes problematic leadership of the National Institute of Mental Health, the liberalism and idealism of the American Psychiatric Association (Glasscote, Sanders, Forstenzer, & Foley, 1964), and the firm conviction of American citizens and their elected representatives that the thrust of human betterment can and must be forwarded in this generation.

References

American Public Health Association, Program Area Committee on Mental Health. *Mental disorders: A guide to control methods.* New York: APHA, 1962.

Bellak, L., & Small, L. *Emergency psychotherapy and brief psychotherapy.* New York: Grune and Stratton, 1965.

Bindman, A. J., & Klebanoff, L. B. Administrative problems in establishing a community mental health program. *American Journal of Orthopsychiatry,* 1959, *30,* 696–711.

Caplan, G. *Principles of preventive psychiatry.* New York: Basic Books, 1964.

Glasscote, R. M., Sanders, D., Forstenzer, H. M., & Foley, A. R. *The community mental health center: An analysis of existing models.* Washington: The Joint Information Service of the American Psychiatric Association and the National Association for Mental Health, 1964.

Goldston, S. E. (Ed.) *Concepts of community psychiatry.* Washington: U.S. Government Printing Office, 1965.

Group for the Advancement of Psychiatry. *Urban America and the planning of mental health services.* Symposium #10. New York: GAP, 1964.

Joint Commission on Mental Illness and Health. *Action for mental health.* New York: Basic Books, 1961.

Kennedy, J. F. Message from the President of the United States relative to mental illness and mental retardation. *American Journal of Psychiatry,* 1964, *120,* 729–737.

Riessman, F., Cohen, J., & Pearl, A. (Eds.) *Mental health of the poor.* New York: Free Press, 1964.

State Mental Health Planning Committee. *Planning comprehensive mental health services in Colorado.* Denver: The Committee, 1965.

Whittington, H. G. *Psychiatry in the American community.* New York: International Universities Press, 1966.

Williams, R. H. (Ed.) *The prevention of disability in mental disorders.* Washington: U.S. Government Printing Office, 1962.

Chapter 5
Mental Health Programs in Schools

Quentin Rae-Grant
and
Lorene A. Stringer

Consultation services to specific groups in the community are forming an important part of the "new wave" in mental health services. It has been repeatedly stated that the aims of consultation differ greatly from those of treatment or supervision.[1] It is essential to remember that the main functions of social institutions such as schools, hospitals, and churches are not those of administering mental health services, although they do have major mental health implications. How mental health weaves into the functioning of these groups becomes an important aspect of the consultant's evaluation of what he would like *to do and what he* can *do in a given situation. The chapter by Dr. Rae-Grant and Miss Stringer makes this clear as they struggle to understand what was going on in themselves and their own agencies as well as in the schools, and how mental health professionals could relate to this important institution in a way consonant both with* their *interests and those of the school personnel.*

[1]Caplan, G. *Principles of preventive psychiatry.* New York: Basic Books, 1964.

Chapter 5

Mental Health Programs in Schools

Quentin Rae-Grant
and
Lorene A. Stringer

Science is not always the handmaiden of progress. The appointment of a committee or the funding of a study to investigate the facts with regard to a problem and to formulate a solution may in fact as much delay and impede action as provide an informed blueprint for future directions. It would be comforting to regard advances in the field of mental health as outcomes of (a) new knowledge based on the findings of empirical research, (b) thoughtful evaluation of alternative struggles, and (c) implementation of programs to fulfill clearly defined aims. More often than not, however, new programs are the outcome of some conviction or idea shared by a few individuals, who then make or seize upon an opportunity to put their conviction into practice. If research is involved at all, it is more likely to be an after-the-fact attempt to evaluate program effects than a rigorous testing of hypotheses through programs designed to prove or disprove them. The relationship between program and research is further complicated by the evolving and changing nature of clinical activities, so that the results of research evaluation, by the time the data are collected and analyzed, are frequently applicable to programs that are no longer in operation. These problems, however, merely complicate the question of research. They do not in any way diminish the gaping need for rigorous and continuing evaluation.

School mental health programs, relatively new developments in the field of mental health, offer a good example of these difficulties. Such programs usually develop out of the strenuous efforts of a few individuals whose convictions converge on some point of need but derive from different preconceptions. Therefore programs are likely to evolve in ways that were quite unforeseen at this beginning and may in fact be diametrically opposed to the original expectations.

The process of instituting school mental health services is analogous to the process of international diplomacy. Each consists of negotiations between two independent and more or less equal organizations, differing in philosophy, in orientation, in methods of practice, and in areas of responsibility, but brought together by some mutual need, often precipitated by external crisis. In the history of school mental health services it is not unusual to find that negotiations have gone on for a considerable length of time, with no visible progress being made, until some crisis arises in the public domain, calling for effective action. A rash of suicides, an epidemic of delinquency, a mushrooming of drug usage, a vivid press exposé, can be more potent in rallying public resources than the most carefully considered and documented appeal for financial program support. It is thus no accident that the leadership for many pioneering endeavors in school mental health programs has come from public health resources, where the community or the public at large is their unit of concern rather than the individual. The incidents that lead to the institution of services, however, are opportunities of expediency rather than basic causes for their creation. Where such services become effective action, there has usually been much previous discussion, laying substantial groundwork for agreement between the two independent systems of school and health services, on the concerns common to both, and on the different resources that each can bring to the implementation of the "crash" program.

The experience of the School Mental Health Services of the St. Louis County Health Department illustrates certain principles of operational development that may prove useful in the construction of general guidelines in other school mental health programs. The St. Louis experience suggests that the most efficient and appropriate services will develop out of negotiations by the specific groups concerned within the specific locality to be serviced. The long-range objective of the planning should not be to achieve uniformity but rather (as Hirschowitz puts it) "to orchestrate diversity."

For a number of years before the School Mental Health Services began, schools and child guidance clinics had been moving gradually toward convergence. In the schools there was increasing concern about school dropouts, delinquency, and poor academic achievement. Because child guidance clinics had successfully treated a few children having such problems, the schools were referring more and more children to clinics, only to find them placed, untreated, on long and rapidly lengthening waiting lists. Children's guidance clinics, on the other hand, had been increasingly pressing the schools to support therapeutic programs for clinic patients and were beginning to glimpse the value of school cooperation and the untapped potential of school resources. Further, survey after survey indicated that at least 10% of children in school were in need of psychiatric help, revealing an alarming discrepancy between services available and the numbers in need of service. Efforts to increase the number of clinics were balked by the limited number of trained professionals, and such additional service as could be gained in this way was vitiated by the huge yearly additions to the school population.

In short, the schools had far greater needs than the resources of the clinics could begin to meet by their traditional, orthodox, time-consuming methods of therapy. The situation called for new methods and experimentation, for services not to individuals but to groups or to whole communities—essentially, for the public health approach. In the St. Louis area two separate developments converged upon this point.

The work of Buchmueller and Gildea (1949) and their colleagues with the parents of behavior problem children in a few city schools suggested that the method of group therapy for parents could significantly ameliorate the problems of the children. In the county the Health Department, under the leadership of the Commissioner of Health, had opened a small child guidance clinic in 1950, which by 1951 was so swamped with referrals that its work had to be limited to diagnostic services only. At the same time, however, the County Council had empowered the Health Department to enter into contracts with individual school districts to make public health nursing services available to the schools at minimal cost. Together the Health Commissioner and Gildea conceived the idea of a school mental health service, funded by contract that would use some of the staff of the Health Department's Child Guidance Clinic to work in schools to reduce behavior problems in children by conducting therapy groups with their parents. Three of the county's 30 school districts contracted for service in the fall of 1951, and a psychologist and a psychiatric social worker from the clinic were assigned to spend part-time in those schools.

The strategy so far consisted simply of an idea, a mandate, an opportunity, a plan of entry, and an exhortation to the two staff members, "Go to it." No ground rules were laid out, no preconceived expectations on either side were subjected to consideration, let alone to open discussion. General rules and expectations were to be elaborated through action. The assumptions of the health professionals (both those who conceived the plan and those who were to carry it out), though not formulated explicitly, were perfectly straightforward: (1) the new program would be like the Buchmueller-Gildea project, (2) three districts demonstrated their readiness for the service by contracting for it, and (3) the staff were trained clinicians and therefore competent to carry out the services in the schools.

That these assumptions were in fact presumptuous became quickly clear. The pilot project had been a free service to the schools; and the workers had, therefore, been free to select, from among the cases referred by the schools, only those that seemed optimally amenable to group therapy. In the county the schools paid for the service and, claiming the right to say which cases should be given priority, referred all of their "basket cases" first. Almost without exception these children had mothers who were the poorest possible candidates for group therapy—or for any other kind of therapy: they wanted none of it.

The school districts, through their superintendents, had indeed contracted for service; but the mental health professionals were employees of the Health Department and not officially within the jurisdiction of the school system. They were outsiders, esoterically knowledgeable, unpredictable, and uncontrollable. There was no fixed place for them in the schools; they interviewed referrals in whatever space they found unoccupied, but all such space was liable to incursions by school personnel so that privacy was accidental at best. Since school days were already filled with customary school activities, superintendents or principals had to go out of their way to arrange time, for themselves or for their teachers, to talk with the mental health professionals; only a few made the effort. In a majority of the schools the clinicians were regularly greeted by the principal with a flustered "My goodness, it's your day already *again?*" followed by an apologetic explanation that he had not yet had time enough to look over the referral forms sent in by the teachers, and then a hopeful suggestion that perhaps the worker could just talk with the teachers that day—maybe the teachers were no longer concerned, maybe the "kiddies" had improved.

Most teachers quickly got the unspoken message and stopped referring. Those who persisted soon found their competence being questioned. At least once a clinician's recommendation for full psychiatric evaluation of a child was flatly rejected by the superintendent, who in the next breath specifically assigned the classroom teacher the responsibility for straightening the child out, even if she "had to lie awake at night to find a way to do it." School resistance was typically more subtle than this, operating subterraneously, but resistance impeded program implementation as much as real receptiveness promoted it. Nowhere were the mental health workers able to establish and maintain mothers' therapy groups. Even if all the schools had been ready, their parent communities were not. If the mental health "outsiders" were mistrusted by most of the schools, they were positively abhorred by practically all of the parents in the three communities.

As for the clinicians, they were trained, yes, but trained to work in the protected setting of the traditional child guidance clinic, where they were concerned only with patient care and responsible only to the other members of the traditional clinic team. They knew little more about schools than they learned from the children and parents referred by the schools, all of whom brought telling evidence of the psychopathogenic nature of school systems and faculties. On the conscious level, the clinicians were grateful to the school administrators for giving them readier access to disturbed children and their parents and teachers, and for the implied willingness to accept and carry out their recommendations. On the unconscious level, they had every intention of protecting those hapless children and their distressed parents against the psychopathogenic forces within the schools.

In short, at the inception of the program the school administrators and the mental health professionals assigned to work in the schools had embarked on courses that seemed bound to end in head-on collision—or capitulation by the one side or the other.

During the second year the two mental health professionals analyzed the problems confronting them. The most pressing problem revolved around the perennial issue of privileged communication. They had been assuring the few students and parents who did come to talk with them that whatever they said would be held fully confidential, only to find themselves later beset by questions from teachers and principals: "Well, what did she tell you?" "What did you find out?" "How does he explain his behavior?" A few of them accepted the clinician's claim to keeping interview content confidential, but most of the school personnel reacted with indignation and suspicion. Not only had they shared all of *their* information with the clinicians, but the schools were *paying* for the clinical skills that could obtain precisely that further information that now the clinicians were withholding. The issue in fact heightened the antagonism between the schools, on the one hand, and the referred children and parents on the other; and the clinicians were caught squarely in the crossfire between the opponents.

The second problem was jurisdictional. The mental health workers, by virtue of their Health Department assignment, were charged with providing appropriate care for emotionally disturbed children. The schools were legally responsible for the school-day-long, school-year-long supervision and education of all students, regardless of whether they were emotionally ill or well. The parents had legal jurisdiction over their own children, plus an imputed moral jurisdiction that was practically beyond challenge. In this obfuscation only two things seemed clear: the mental health professionals had responsibility but no authority, and the children had no jurisdiction at all.

A third problem had to do with the mental health workers' professional identity. They were of the clinic but not in it. They were in the schools but not of them. They were in a professional no-man's-land that, strangely enough, had not been visible to anyone until these two people appeared in it. They were suspect figures; in the clinicians' eyes they were obviously not clinicians; in the educators' eyes, obviously not educators; even in their own eyes they were unidentifiable vagrants.

And yet, in spite of these problems, and quite as if the problems were on one plane, and the day-by-day work on another, a few parents and children were being helped, a few teachers were seeking consultation, and student therapy groups had been formed and were meeting weekly in all three high schools. Old friendships with clinicians were maintained, and here and there in the schools new friendships developed between the mental health workers and a principal or a superintendent. Out of these latter friendships came a more sympathetic understanding of the educators' problems, and a closer identification with their aims, to the point where a new school mental health policy could be formulated—namely, that the mental health workers' central concern must be the school itself, the whole school, not just the disturbed children in it. They stopped promising confidentiality to the people they interviewed, they explicitly identified themselves with the school and its aims—and they found that this detracted not a whit from their effectiveness in interviewing, while it markedly improved their relationships with school personnel.

In an earlier paper we called this the period of capitulation on the part of the mental health workers (Rae-Grant & Stringer, 1964). In retrospect that seems not entirely accurate. It *was* over-correction of the position that the mental health workers had initially taken and then found untenable; and it was, no doubt, a bid to gain the schools' acceptance: but it was also a perfectly sound public health approach that had simply not been recognized before. In general, mental health professionals have been oddly laggard about concerning themselves with keeping well children well.

At this point when, after two years of trial and error, a reasonable basis for developing a program appeared to have been attained but no modus operandi had yet been settled upon, science entered the picture. It entered by two quite different avenues and had marked impact on program development in two different and totally unforeseen ways. Dr. John C. Glidewell joined the Health Department staff to mount an NIMH-funded research project "to evaluate the effectivensss of mothers' therapy groups in modifying behavior problems of elementary school children." The research design called for the extension of service into eight school districts. With no questions asked, the three contracting districts renewed their contracts for an additional three years. With no questions, also, five more districts signed contracts.

The clinical psychologist assigned to the schools went back to the clinic, unwilling to be a part of what he alternatively saw as gamesmanship or a "farce." The psychiatric caseworker protested that there was no "effectiveness" to evaluate, that this was talking to the wind when the wind was blowing. Two more psychiatric caseworkers were recruited to work in the schools, one on a full-time and the other on a part-time basis. With eight districts now to be covered, it was no longer possible for the staff people to work in both clinic and schools; and they were effectively (though unofficially) separated from the clinic staff. To escape living in a professional no-man's-land, the senior school mental health worker began to speak of the program as the School Mental Health Services. The name never received official recognition; but over the years and simply by dint of frequent usage it identified the program and the professionals working in it, lending them desperately needed support as they tried to find appropriate roles to fit into.

Early in the 1955–56 school year Dr. Glidewell's project showed that there were no mothers' therapy groups in progress in the schools, and the Health Department planners were at last shocked into listening to the field staff. Further necessary concessions were finally granted. A psychiatrist from the Child Guidance Clinic was designated Psychiatric Consultant to the staff, and the staff itself was expanded under an agreed policy that full-time members would devote three days a week to work in the schools and two days in the Health Department in program and staff development activities. These activities included clinical conferences on the children they had referred in from the schools and staff meetings devoted to trying to formulate what the staff did in the schools, why they chose certain approaches, under which circumstances these worked effectively and under which they failed, and how they might better implement what they saw now as the common or at least overlapping aims of education and of mental health.

While Dr. Glidewell's research was having these effects on the organizational and logistic structure of the service, the second research approach was underway in the most cooperative of the first three contracting districts. This was research by accident rather than by plan. The senior mental health worker, alarmed by the prospect that Dr. Glidewell's work might well terminate the school service unless something could be done to demonstrate its worth, had begun an intensive study of the school records of children referred to her. As a clinician, she had been from the outset disturbed over the school's policy of routinely promoting children from one grade to the next, regardless of whether they had mastered the work well enough to have earned promotion. Obviously, she could not simply challenge the school administrators' cherished philosophy that lay behind this policy. In the school's own records, however, there was stark evidence that achievement throughout the elementary grades was growing poorer year after year. This evidence provided entry into a long series of weekly consultations with the school administrators, eventuating in a decision to test automatic promotion against a selective retention system.

Three outcomes of that experiment are worth noting: (a) it was successful enough to lead to a revision of school policy on promotions and to demonstrate that school policy could be signally effective in reducing the incidence of academic casualties (Stringer, 1960); (b) it proved that it was both possible and profitable for school administrators and mental health professionals to engage in collaborative problem-solving approaches to issues of concern to both; and (c) the instrument (Academic Progress Chart) devised to evaluate the results of retentions versus social promotions gave promise of being an inexpensive and efficient screening instrument for the early detection of emotional disturbances in school children (Stringer, 1959).

This small study had no immediate impact on either the staff or the school mental health program, but the Academic Progress Chart attracted Dr. Glidewell's interest and he initiated efforts to obtain NIMH funding to explore its potential as a screening tool. When that application was approved in 1959, the senior caseworker left the school service to collaborate on the research.

In effect, for a period of almost 10 years there were two main approaches, one visible and the other not so visible. The visible one was the School Mental

Health Services, slowly but steadily expanding as new districts contracted for service and as older districts increased the amount of service for which they contracted. In spite of staff turnovers, both in the Health Department and in the schools, more and more lines of communication were opened up between mental health personnel and school personnel. Community attitudes toward the service shifted gradually toward more acceptance. It was a slow and laborious process, and the work remained predominantly case focused and pathology oriented. But the mental health staff stayed persistently with the task and its difficulties, completely convinced that sometime, somewhere, they would find their efforts richly productive.

Less visibly, the research investigation continued. By 1962 it had developed findings showing that the sickest children in the schools had been already sick when they first entered school and that 61% of the cases on referral to the School Mental Health Services could have been referred, on the basis of their Academic Progress Chart patterns, anywhere from one year to eight years before they actually were referred (Glidewell & Stringer, 1962). Earlier detection of emotional illness in school children *was* possible, and it was possible also that mental health intervention at the kindergarten or first-grade level might often prevent the development of serious disturbance.

These findings wakened recollection of service experiences, the implication of which had gone unrecognized at the time. In schools that held group orientation meetings for mothers of incoming kindergartners and introduced the mental health worker as one of the special services staff, mothers had shown themselves eager to seek mental health consultation, not because they considered their children disturbed but because they wanted to keep them from becoming disturbed, they wanted the know-how that they thought the mental health worker could give. Many such mothers referred themselves; and as with self-referrals among high school students, they proved highly receptive and able to make swift and effective use of the offered help.

There emerged from all this a first formulation of the concept that a school mental health program ought to concern itself at least as much with the positive promotion of mental health in children as with alleviating emotional illnesses (Stringer, 1964). In theory this formulation was favorably received by the schools, but in practice the schools continued to swamp the mental health staff with referrals of their most seriously disturbed children. The mental health workers, sharing the school's concern about these casualties, continued to spend all their efforts on attempting to ameliorate deeply entrenched illnesses. The concept was not lost, however. The newly appointed psychiatric director of the service saw its possibilities and asked the research project director to be consultant to the service, attending staff meetings and making available to the field staff any salient research findings for whatever use they could make of them in practice. This reestablished communication between the research and the service, although for a year or so longer there were no new and salient findings, nothing change-inducing in the communication.

The next important development in the research investigation came, most unexpectedly, from a sizeable group of mothers who had volunteered for individual research interviews about the children selected for a sample to be studied. Although they had been told to expect no individual help for themselves or their children, two out of every three mothers spontaneously commented that they had gained personal benefit from the interview experience; and a significant number proposed that if such interviews were conducted with every mother as her child entered school, the benefits accruing to the children would be invaluable. Again the clear message was: Help us to keep our children well.

Out of this there developed, again with NIMH funding, a new project combining a demonstration service and a research evaluation of the service potential for the primary prevention of emotional illnesses in children. Called "Mothers as Colleagues in School Mental Health Work," it had three central aims: first, to add to basic knowledge of child development patterns all that interested mothers could contribute to it; second, to reach toward earlier detection of incipient disturbances in children; and, third, to reduce parental defensiveness about need for psychiatric help by enlisting parental collaboration in a mental *health* effort. Research interviews held before a child was evaluated by the school could be emotionally as well as intellectually neutral. Focused more on a child's psychosocial resources than on his symptomatology, the interviews could introduce mothers to positive concepts of mental health, while at the same time introducing them to a mental health consultant who would remain available to them if at any subsequent time they wanted to return to him for consultation. The mental health consultant would be similarly available for consultation to teachers. The new formulation could perhaps be stated thus: since experience has amply demonstrated that mental health is effective only when and where it is wanted, the sensible thing to do is to make it available on request—to parents, teachers, students, school administrators—and to direct the efforts first to where the needs are felt and recognized.

At present (fall, 1967) although the potential of this project for primary prevention still remains to be evaluated, there is conclusive evidence that such a service works well in a school that wants it. The School Mental Health Services staff, wearied by long and discouraging experience in working with serious disturbances and excited by this and their own experimentations with inviting self-referrals, are successfully persuading more and more school administrators to give contract-time priorities to self-referrals, with particular focus on the earliest school years.

One further new direction is becoming quite clear. In both the demonstration project and the ongoing school program, teacher requests for case consultations have been increasing in what is almost geometric progression. These consultations not only result in help to the children on whom they focus, but they also promote the exchange of special knowledge and an understanding between school personnel and mental health personnel. Educators clearly see a need for such consultations, a need quite possibly so widespread that it cannot in any foreseeable future be met by case consultations with mental health professionals. There are simply not enough adequately skilled and experienced school mental health professionals to do the job. And yet there is a way out. Teachers and principals are the front-line people in the field of school mental health, and constitute a mental health resource that has scarcely been tapped. A few intensive workshops, of two weeks duration, have shown that given intelligible and relevant theory school professionals can translate theory into practice with precision, ingenuity, and originality that mental health professionals would be hard put to match.

The obvious next strategy, therefore, is to develop programs to provide the kinds of mental health theory, knowledge, and practices that will enable educators, in training and in service, to actualize their tremendous potential for both the primary prevention of emotional illnesses and the positive promotion of mental health in school children.

In any growing program there are always problems. Often the process of solving one problem reveals two others to be solved. In addition, once-solved problems cannot be counted upon to remain solved; when new people—parents or educators or mental health professionals—enter the program area, they bring old problems back to life and challenge old solutions, so that a process of retesting is continually going on. This process seems an indispensable part of healthy growth. In this sense the school program in St. Louis County is still an adolescent; but from the foregoing account of its development thus far, five sets of considerations can be elucidated, perhaps to serve as guidelines in the development of other programs, and perhaps to reduce the need to repeat the same mistakes again and again.

1. *With respect to entry*. The delineation of formal arrangements merely opens the door to exploration of the field and of the forces deployable within it. Certainly, to work in the schools requires the agreement of the superintendent, and to work with classroom teachers requires the convinced approval of the school principal. But this is only giving the mental health consultant opportunity to learn about the school system. In return, the consultant had better be candid about his need to learn about the system, had better be able to say, as a mature professional, that he can function efficiently and be of help to the school only if he is fully acquainted with what the school itself has to offer. He needs to understand the administrative organization of the system, how the administrators and the classroom teachers and the special educational personnel and the custodial staff relate to each other, because this provides essential information about areas of strength and weakness within the system that will determine the points of entry where the mental health impact can be significant.

But if he is to get a gut feeling for the system, if he is to be aware of its potential for both development and booby traps, he must also be able to discern the attitudes and preconceptions, expressed and unexpressed, within the school personnel and in himself. He must familiarize himself with the history of previous transactions that have taken place between the school and other mental health services. He must know who the key individuals are within the system, and what are their public and what their private stances.

Similarly, the consultant's interpretation of the proposed mental health program is only a tentative formulation. School personnel must be invited to indicate what, from their point of view, are the areas of primary concern, the questions and issues that are most troublesome—not with any promise that the consultant will devote his initial efforts to these areas and issues, but so that he can examine the presenting problems for possible ways of handling them. The tactical points of entry to them may be very different from the areas themselves. But to gain permission to take these different points of entry requires full elaboration of the reasons and the documentation therefore, the results to be expected therefrom, the alternative choices from among which this one recommendation is made, and the enlistment of the school's consent to the recommended direction of movement.

The format of program, in other words, should not be determined by the school alone or by the mental health professional alone, but should be a natural and not too uncomfortable outgrowth of the needs of both and of their capacities to form working arrangements to meet their common needs. A choice point of entry and format of operation has implications both as to who will be served and, even more important, who will not be served. Though the choices may be dictated by necessity, there needs to be continual review of where the expectations are being fulfilled, of where, in fact, the predictions of access to high risk areas remain valid over the course of time. Interest in a particular sector of work can carry mental health professionals along on a wave of enthusiasm, but if simultaneously that choice has withheld help from an enlarging group in need, the enthusiasm will not be shared or supported by the school, which carries responsibility for the total school population. At entry, then, the format should be conditional, exploratory, and with explicit provision for review and revision as time and experience dictate.

2. *With respect to implementation.* In any program where mental health resources are limited, certain difficult choices have to be made as to where to use those resources and how to allocate priorities to needs. Made preceptively, these choices may be not only ineffective, but may also line off a very limited sector of opportunity. Made judiciously, they can lead to flexible and sequential staging of an increasingly wide range of activities. It is important to delineate what services will be provided; and it is vital to formulate a parallel answer, as to what cannot and will not be provided at a particular period in time. For mental health professionals with their urge to help, it is emotionally stressful to enunci-

ate explicitly the limitations of their mandate and resources, but to imply by vagueness more than can be offered is to invite eventual disillusionment and defeat.

In young school programs there is always a contest between demands for direct service and need for consultative services. Direct case services are enormously time-consuming; and yet, as Glidewell has pointed out (Glidewell, 1959), some direct service may well be essential to gaining initial acceptance within the school system. It is analogous, he suggests, to trial by ordeal—before school personnel can regard the mental health worker as competent, he must demonstrate what he can do with the individual and usually very difficult cases first referred to him.

Commitment to a consultation approach is the only practical way to reach the large volume of problems in the school mental health field. But most mental health professionals are trained for direct service, not for consultation. Few of them move into consultation without considerable anxiety about their competence in it; and many retreat from it, back to direct service because, although it narrows the definition of the mandate and is often less appropriate for the needs of the school, it is more comfortably suited to the competence of the practitioner. Few remain in consultation for long, however, without finding convincing evidence of its value. The passing contact in the corridor, the brief question from a teacher, the informal discussion after the formal meeting, or the casual question on administrative policy—these contacts have far less visibility than they deserve because they are capable of changing the whole shape and direction of a program.

Regular consultation with school principals is indispensable. It provides a mechanism for pinpointing needs, for clarifying the limits of resources, and for making the hard and often painful choices between competing alternatives, while recognizing that, at least for the moment, some needs will have to go unmet. Out of such recurrent assessments, such deliberate allocations of resources, and specific decisions about priorities, the principal and his mental health consultant come to understand better what each may fairly and reasonably expect of the other.

There should be no illusions about the complexity of school mental health programs or about how severely they tax the energy, the skill, and the daring of the mental health professionals. They go into schools to help the schools, and they are expected to provide help despite the lack of an organized body of knowledge about mental health work in schools. They must proceed along presumptive lines instead of waiting for cast-iron information before they act. They must, therefore, have an ability to tolerate ambiguity (not to be overwhelmed by it), and a willingness to proceed experimentally, but energetically, with a commitment to follow through to evaluation of whatever they do.

3. *With respect to the community.* It is treacherously easy for both educators and mental health professionals to consider the community as the more or less

passive recipient of professional activities, or even as the reluctant or stiffly resistive target of professional aims. The fact is that these professionals, when they behave like self-seeking politicians, can exhaust themselves with efforts and still achieve nothing whatsoever in the way of results, unless the community happens to want what they want.

In any community mental health program, therefore, the professionals will do well to focus first of all on listening to the community—to its behavior as well as to its verbalized statements, to its covert attitudes as well as to its publicly expressed opinions. They will do well not only to listen to the community (the School Mental Health Services staff did that) but also to hear and understand and respond appropriately and promptly (the School Mental Health Services staff took years to do that). In the final analysis, it is from the community that the mandate comes, whatever the mandate may be. The professionals can and should publish what they know about the community's educational and mental health situation, and can and should propose measures to better it; but they cannot devise measures that will be both effective and accepted unless they are constantly and sensitively hearing what the community says to them. Education and mental health are far from having final answers, though they have arrived at a commitment to work jointly in the search for answers. A parallel effort is not so good as a concerted effort, and to develop a concerted effort they must enlist the active collaboration of the community.

4. *With respect to mental health in education.* From their formal training there are four significant contributions that mental health workers can bring and, given permission, deploy usefully to the health of the school system. The first is knowledge of human growth and development, both in its healthy aspects and in its disturbed aspects, and a knowledge of the stages of development and the normal crises that children have to meet, face, and work through if they are to mature. The second is knowledge of the contribution of emotional factors to the success or failure of a child in learning. The third is an understanding of interpersonal process (be it between child and teacher, child and parents, parents and teachers, teachers and teachers, teachers and principals, or school personnel and mental health personnel) and an appreciation of the ways in which the interpersonal process can be understood, made more explicit, and therefore more useful in dealing with the tasks at hand.

A less tangible but probably equally significant contribution derives from the nature of the training and practice that mental health workers bring to this field. This focuses on the ability to tolerate ambiguity and uncertainty and the knowledge that, in dealing with the intangibles of mental health, forced clarity may be more impeding than recognizing and struggling with uncertainty. The mental health professional can demonstrate the issues of uncertainty for dealing with particular issues. He can show how important it is to avoid premature closure that does not represent a solution and encourage the necessary continuing, devoted examination, trial, experimentation, and evaluation. The quick decision may shelve the real question. Recognition of the danger of premature closure promotes efforts to search for a sound solution and quietly accepts the awful truth that immediate, dramatic, and specific panaceas are few and far between.

Other significant contributions will derive from the style of operation of each individual school program, generating in practice the specific details of possibility and effectiveness. There is no question about the value of initial planning, of information gathering, and of the delineation of tenative contracts, but hopes and plans must be subjected to the test of experience and action is therefore a vital ingredient in a developing school mental health service. The drawing board is good only for planning entry. Not until the service is launched and there has been action enough to allow for beginning appraisals of effectiveness does it become possible to see alternatives and to debate their relative merits and then to make more specific plans and to implement them more adroitly. A viable, growing school mental health program is necessarily a grassroots operation in the schools and in the school community.

Until quite recently mental health personnel have considered psychotherapy the only definitive and effective kind of intervention. In the context of school work, as in other mental health operation, however, it is more appropriate to regard psychotherapy as "the surgery of mental health," to be employed only where other less intensive methods have been tried and have failed (Rae-Grant, Gladwin, & Bower, 1966). To continue the long-existing trend in specialized clinics towards "psychiatric over-kill"—that process by which previously scarce time is devoted to a small minority of cases, to achieve ends defined by the worker rather than derived by patient or client—is to invite a slow-but-sure crippling and eventual defeat of mental health efforts in the schools. It is no more appropriate in the schools than anywhere else to deny pathology where pathology exists, but to zero in on pathology in the schools is to invite premature closure, stifling healthy program growth. The more appropriate aim in schools is to zero in on children's coping strengths and their psychosocial resources, to learn how to identify them and promote their optimal development and in this way enhance the social competence of the children.

Fortunately for this aim, the climate for school mental health work has changed dramatically over the past 10 to 15 years. As a result of several successful programs, an atmosphere of much greater receptivity now prevails. Mental health workers are now more welcome in schools, and schools are altering their conception of where mental health can make the most substantial contribution. Mental health workers, also, are altering their conception of where and how they can be most helpful, and increasingly they are recognizing that their greatest leverage is in encouraging school administrators to develop policies and practice that will support the healthy growth of the total school population. As quickly as it is pointed out to them, school administrators see that the schools have the greatest immediate potential for the primary prevention of emotional disturbance and that it is education, not psychiatry, that can bring the best resources to the positive promotion of mental health. Schools are not comfortable with psychiatric processes, but to undertake responsibility for using the educational process to promote the better development of children's mental health—this they are ready and willing to do.

Toward this end they are increasingly, and most encouragingly, inviting mental health consultation. They have a cross-sectional knowledge of children's behavior, and the management skills and techniques for dealing with children. Mental health consultants have a longitudinal knowledge of how children grow and what forces shape their growth. Wherever these two complementary resources learn to work together, the schools themselves become enormously potent forces in supporting children's growth toward mental health.

5. *With respect to education in mental health.* Increasingly, also, both administrators and classroom teachers are asking for mental health workshops, wanting clearer understanding of the meanings of children's behaviors, convinced that if they can obtain that, they will see more available alternatives and be able to take more flexible approaches to the problems that they have to handle on a daily basis. In these requests they are not asking for courses in psychiatric diagnosis and treatment; they are asking how they can become more effective teachers and how, as teachers, they can deal with 30 children at a time and give to each of the 30 the sensitive understanding and guidance that he needs and has a right to. (Fifteen years ago, few teachers were asking for anything more than to be relieved of their most troublesome students.)

The invitation is open, but few mental health professionals feel competent enough to accept it. Workshops that are in effect a series of case conferences have been minimally effective, eliciting interest and sometimes argument and challenge but having little if any carry-over into the classroom. There is not, as yet, enough empirical evidence available to indicate what other kinds of teacher workshops may be more effective, but at least one other kind is enthusiastically received—the kind that attempts to give intelligible and usable theory and leaves with the educators the responsibility for perceiving how best to apply it.

It is critically important for the leader of such workshops to recognize that helping teachers to understand children means asking them to remember how they felt as children. Sensitizing them to the meanings of children's behavior invariably includes sensitizing them to the meanings of their own behavior as children and as adults, an always intensely personal and sometimes very painful process. This can be dangerous if it is required of people who are unwilling to lend themselves to it. The group leader must know how to leave the workshop participants free to engage in discussion when they want and equally free to disengage themselves from discussion when that is their choice. In addition, therefore, to having solid knowledge of what schools are like, the group leader of such a workshop must understand group dynamics and interpersonal relationships and be alert to the phenomena of transference and counter-transference, because both of these come quickly into play and must be handled with care and skill. Only as this kind of sensitivity in the group leader becomes clear to the participants can they begin to feel confidence in him and encouraged to share their own experiences with the group, and so to discover the mutually supportive nature of the group experience.

Typically, such workshops begin on an intellectual level and focus upon children and on children's problems; but as children's problems are interpreted in terms of their feelings, there occurs the first sharing of personal experiences in the group situation. These are almost invariably unhappy experiences, but they are listened to sympathetically and as they elicit further sharing from other group members much of the sting of unhappiness appears to vanish. Participants can then be stimulated to remember moments of pure enjoyment, and the sharing of these in the group situation becomes a highly charged and liberating emotional experience.

Perhaps the key to the apparent effectiveness of workshops of this type lies in the fact that most elementary school teachers retain a considerable quality of the childlike in themselves. They tend to relate to the group leader as they would like their students to relate to them, to be as responsive to the leader as they would have their students be to them. In this kind of emotional climate they are open to new ideas and new perceptions, and they use these creatively both in the ongoing group process of the workshop itself and in their planning for their next teaching assignments. If careful research evaluation substantiates the apparent value of this kind of workshop, another broad new strategy is available for school mental health work.

When it is remembered that each child is expected to be under school supervision for at least 14,000 hours of his formative years, it is clear that the schools have an enormous potential for shaping the future. Not only do they communicate cognitive skills, but, complementary to the family, they firm up the processes of socialization and strengthen the coping capacities of the individual child. The power vested in them by law is tremendous, as is the responsibility placed upon them. Few use more than a small portion of their power, partly out of concern lest they misuse it. Rightly awed by their power and responsibility, the schools are now turning to mental health and the behavior sciences in the hope that they will point out ways in which this power can better be used to help children become socially effective and productive adults. To help them achieve this goal, specific operational practices have to be designed through cooperative action programs in each specific school district and school. Research plays a key role as the monitor of action enthusiasms, the focuses of the clear light of reality, and the pointer to both deficits in practice and new directions for attention and implementation. Only as action enthusiasms are buttressed by scientific objectivity can we move ahead. The field is now open, and the mental-health professions have been invited in. The work is arduous, and the outcome cannot be guaranteed, but if mental health is to fulfill its mandate to increase emotional strength in individuals and if the school is to fulfill its mandate to develop competent, informed, and effective citizens, we must move ahead.

References

Buchmueller, A. D., & Gildea, M. C. L. A group therapy project with parents of behavior problem children in public schools. *American Journal of Psychiatry*, 1949, *106*, 46–53.

Glidewell, J. C. The entry problem in consultation. *Journal of Social Issues*, 1959, *15* (2), 50–59.

Glidewell, J. C., & Stringer, Lorene A. Progress Report III, OM–188. St. Louis County Health Department, August, 1962.

Rae-Grant, Q. A., & Stringer, L. A. Design for a new orthopsychiatric discipline. *American Journal of Orthopsychiatry*, 1964, *34*, 722–729.

Rae-Grant, Q. A., Gladwin, T., & Bower, E. Mental health, social competence, and the war on poverty. *American Journal of Orthopsychiatry*, 1966, *36*, 652–664.

Stringer, L. A. Academic progress as an index of mental health. *Journal of Social Issues*, 1959, *15* (1), 16–29.

Stringer, L. A. Report on retentions program. *Elementary School Journal*, 1960, *60*, 370–375.

Stringer, L. A. Role of the school and the community. *Journal of School Health*, 1963, *33*, (9), 385–390.

Stringer, L. A. Parent-child relations in the early school years. *Social Work*, 1964, *9* (2), 98–104.

Stringer, L. A. School policies and practices: Our most neglected resource for better education and mental health. *Journal of School Health*, 1967, *37*, 440–448.

Chapter 6
More Than Psychiatry:
A Rural Program

Frank Kiesler

In recent years the urban and suburban centers have become the focus of many of our concerns, sometimes at the expense of the rural areas that still form an important element in the United States. Dr. Kiesler shows how some of the problems in setting up services in rural areas may be unique. For example, unlike urban areas where, as Dr. Whittington says, because of the density of the population it becomes necessary to draw arbitrary lines to hold to the upper limits of existing legislation, rural areas often cannot meet the lower limits of the legislation to get adequate funding.

However, in his honest, detailed presentation of successes and failures, Dr. Kiesler reveals that many of the problems of working with rural communities do not differ markedly from those in other areas. He tells how, in his eagerness to respond to community needs, he unexpectedly became identified with certain elements of the community at the expense of others. He discusses the ambivalence and resistances of various interest groups within the community. He talks about how he sometimes had to retrace his steps and alter his strategy in order to work out problems in implementation. He shows how, with a small staff, it became necessary to identify early what could and could not be done and what the direction of the service would be. But above all, he reveals the sincerity, personal involvement, flexibility, and genuine appreciation of the human elements within the community that should not be ignored as an important ingredient in the success of any new program.

Chapter 6

More Than Psychiatry:
A Rural Program

Frank Kiesler

In 1957 an act[1] of the Minnesota State Legislature authorized the Minnesota Department of Public Welfare to distribute grants-in-aid to assist communities to develop and operate local mental health programs. The program-fostering intent of the law has enabled the state to help pay for much more than psychiatry.[2] Broad-spectrum mental health problem-solving concepts have been most fully implemented in rural areas where functional boundaries more distinctly delineate communities with populations small enough to make total population-focused efforts feasible. The history of implementation in one rural northern Minnesota program area illustrates some of the formulations, some of the problems, and some of the strategies.

Setting

Occupying a glaciated area of forests and lakes, approximately 220 miles long, and extending from the middle of the state due north to the Canadian border, are three vertically stacked northern Minnesota counties—Aitkin, Itasca, and Koochiching. Together, these counties contain about 10,000 square

---

[1]Minnesota Statutes, 1957, Section 245.61 to 245.69.

[2]In the years since 1957, 23 community mental health programs have been established to serve areas containing more than 95% of the population of Minnesota. Common to both urban and rural programs is local proprietorship. Each program has been organized and operated by the community area it serves. Each is supported with local funds supplemented by matching state grants-in-aid. Eligibility for matching grants is determined by the State Department of Public Welfare through annual review of program plans, budgets, financing plans, and professional staff qualifications. Key personnel of the Department of Public Welfare, clearly recognizing that the search for better answers can never end, have consistently encouraged innovative diversity in program development. In the beginning, there were no innovators. The first mental health professionals employed by local community mental health boards preferred the safety of familiar psychiatric practice boundaries. Some latecomers, espousing public health concepts, viewed psychiatric services as one component of population-focused mental health problem-solving programs.

miles and 64,000 people.[3] Grand Rapids, with approximately 8,000 people, is the Itasca county seat and the largest town in the area.

Historically, the area was first opened by the French, who sent missionaries and fur traders to live with the Indians. Only 100 years ago Scandinavian and Finnish immigrants began to log off the white pine forests and establish the first permanent settlements. Later Ukrainians came to the Canadian border area. When the major pine stands were almost gone and replaced by second growth pulpwood, papermaking had become a rapidly growing industry in the border town of International Falls and in Grand Rapids. Attracted early in this century by jobs in eastern Itasca County's open pit iron mines were Serbians and Italians, who replaced many of the Finnish who had cleared land and turned to dairy farming. Determined that their children would have better opportunities, these early citizens developed sufficient political leverage to funnel increased taxes on industry into the creation and operation of some of the best public school systems in the nation. Since World War I, industrial expansion and union organization have gone hand-in-hand, neither side daring to relax its grip lest the other gain the advantage. One product of union contract negotiations has been an exceptionally high standard of medical care and hospitalization insurance coverage.

Today's sustaining industries are iron mining, papermaking, and year-round outdoor recreation. Large-scale crop farming is not feasible, and dairy farming has diminished since World War II. Many lush pastures, once so laboriously cleared, have now become Christmas tree farms. Despite a slump in iron mining in the first half of the sixties, pending construction of processing plants for lower grades of ore, the general economy has remained healthy and has shown continued growth. Reduced employment in mining accounted for much of Itasca County's population loss between 1960 and 1966. There was also some acceleration of a previous gradual population shift from the outlying areas and the smallest towns to the larger towns.

Prior to 1959, in the whole three-county area, there had never been resident mental health specialists nor specific mental health or retardation facilities of any kind. Persons needing the services of mental health specialists went to Duluth or to Minneapolis for private care. Public care also required going outside of the area to the Moose Lake State Hospital, to state hospitals for the retarded, to the Veterans Hospitals, or to the University of Minnesota Hospitals. A few children were admitted to residential treatment centers in Duluth.

[3] County	1960 Census	1966 Estimates
Aitkin	12,000	11,500
Itasca	38,000	34,700
Koochiching	18,000	17,800
	68,000	64,000

Traveling psychometrists from the state department of public welfare supplied limited psychological testing services to county welfare departments and schools. There were neither school social workers nor school psychologists. Most mental health problems had been handled locally by family doctors, county welfare caseworkers, school administrators, school counselors, school nurses, classroom teachers, clergymen, attorneys, law enforcement personnel, county nurses, visiting vocational rehabilitation counselors, veterans service officers, and others having contact with troubled people. Almost all were sure that the job could be done better by "real"mental health professionals.

Inception

In 1958, stimulated by the efforts of others elsewhere in the state to apply the provisions of the 1957 state enabling act to local mental health program development, three Grand Rapids professionals began to explore the possibility of organizing something for their own area. One was the Itasca County welfare director, another was the superintendent of schools, and the third was a general medical practitioner who was also the part-time Itasca County public health officer. Although the state enabling act spoke of community mental health *programs,* all implementation efforts in other areas of the state had immediately become facility oriented. Similarly translating the statute, the three Itasca County promoters began to sell a community mental health *center.* They envisioned a psychiatric service facility staffed by professionals who could employ direct diagnostic and treatment methods to solve mental health problems in the community.

Because the state enabling act required a population base of at least 50,000 and because Aitkin and Koochiching were the only adjoining counties not already involved in negotiations with other counties, both were invited to join Itasca County in setting up a mental health center. By 1959, these three counties had entered into a preliminary fiscal agreement among themselves and with the state and had appointed three persons each to a Tri-County Mental Health Board.[4] This nine-member statutory board was charged with preparing a preliminary program plan, proposing an initial budget and financing plan, obtaining basic funding commitments from all three county boards of commissioners, submitting an application for a state grant-in-aid, finding office space, and recruiting professional personnel. The director of the Itasca County Welfare

---

[4]In 1963, the members of the Tri-County Mental Health Board formed a nonprofit public service corporation and constituted themselves the Board of Directors of the Northland Mental Health Center, Inc. Then, taking advantage of a provision of the 1957 enabling act, they replaced the original nine member statutory board with a larger Northland Mental Health Board (now 13 members) in order to gain better representation from the three counties. Corporate structure also made it possible for the board to enter into contracts and hold title to property. The name was changed in order to eliminate restrictive connotations of the word "county."

Department was elected first chairman of the board. He did most of the initial organizational work. Because of its functionally central location, Grand Rapids was designated the site of the proposed Tri-County Mental Health Center. Estimates of potentially available funds suggested that no more than three professional staff members could ever be employed.

By September, 1959, a psychiatric social worker from Illinois had arrived. One month later he was joined by a Canadian clinical psychologist, who was appointed acting program director. The author, who was then Director of Psychiatric Education at the University of Minnesota Medical School in Minneapolis, was originally asked by the board chairman to help find a suitable psychiatrist. Attracted by the response of the board and staff to his questions and suggestions regarding *program* focus and organization, the author applied for the job. He then served as consultant until he could move to Grand Rapids in July of 1960 and become full-time psychiatrist and program director.

Program Concept

Since the participating counties had agreed to pay for a facility to make psychiatric services more readily available, it was originally assumed that all of these psychiatric services would be delivered by mental health professionals employed to staff the facility. From the point of view of a three-man professional staff, this was not feasible. We found it necessary to stimulate a shift from a psychiatric facility focus to a public health program concept involving all of the mental health influencing resources in the community. Fortunately, the board was receptive.

When we suggested to the board that accepting all requests for direct psychiatric service would quickly lock us away from the community behind filled appointment schedules and a growing waiting list, it was agreed that emphasis on direct service could make only a small dent in the mental health problems of the population of our three counties. Board members from the two outlying counties were particularly concerned that we not become captives of Itasca County patients. All board members expressed concern that the prevalence, incidence, and severity of many kinds of mental health problems, ranging from a potpourri of marital and childrearing difficulties to a fuzzy melange of criminal acts and disabling psychotic behavior, might be increasing.

Therefore, in a total community program context, we defined three tasks. One was the task of caring for all existing and emerging adaptive casualties, *the clinical task*. Another was the task of reducing the numbers of newly emerging casualties, *the primary preventive task*. Secondary and tertiary preventive concepts were embodied in the clinical task. The third we defined as the task of devising ways to determine baselines and trends for the prevalence and incidence of specific kinds of casualty behavior, to define the characteristics of high risk groups, and to determine to what extent changes in prevalence and incidence might be related to various problem-solving approaches. This is *the measurement task.*

Whether or not their personnel recognize it, all of the mental health influencing resources of every community are concerned, both singly and in concert, with all three of these tasks. However, because in 1959 in our three-county area only the clinical task was in reasonably clear focus, we first tried to define how the whole community might best address itself to finding better solutions for a whole range of already existing and constantly emerging adaptive problems. Most of these problems neither required nor responded to formal psychiatric intervention. More solutions than psychiatry could provide were needed. At the same time, there also were more psychiatric problems than three mental health specialists could handle. We needed a rationale for assignment of priorities.

Our basic premise was that the effective mental health influencing manpower force in any community consists of *all* of the professionals who try to help troubled people solve their adaptive problems. In our three counties we had counted more than 300 such professionals, including the medical practitioners, clergymen, attorneys, sheriffs and police chiefs, judges, welfare administrators and caseworkers, county nurses, school administrators, school counselors, school nurses, employment and vocational rehabilitation counselors, and the veterans service officers. Extending this basic premise, we took the position that we mental health specialists should most properly be regarded as three additions to this already functioning mental health influencing manpower force.

Our second premise was that most troubled people usually can obtain more useful help if they first turn to local primary professionals instead of to a central specialty facility. Therefore, we reasoned, even when specialty personnel become available, local primary professionals should not only continue to do as much mental health work as previously, but they should also learn how to do it with greater proficiency.

Our third premise was that we three mental health specialists could be of most value to the whole community if major portions of our time could be deliberately allocated to assisting the rest of the manpower force in increasing its effectiveness, particularly in the pursuit of early detection of disorder and early intervention (secondary prevention). Because such a commitment to the whole manpower force and to the whole spectrum of adaptive problems with which the total manpower force was concerned would severely restrict our direct clinical service activities, we needed to find a way to provide more direct psychiatric services than we could supply. Since all medical services in our area are delivered from a private practice base, we concluded that the most natural way to fill the gap would be through recruitment of a psychiatrist for the private practice of general psychiatry. Economically, the area could support such a practice.

Logical as all of these premises seemed to us, we had to recognize that the rest of the manpower force could not be expected to translate them spontaneously into practice. We knew that familiar patterns of referral to specialists, and even dumping of troublesome problems, would continue until it could be demonstrated that the demands of the clinical task could be satisfied by other approaches. The history of the first several months of program implementation illustrates a test of this hypothesis.

Program Implementation

Pleading the need for time to become acquainted with the area and decide on a modus operandi the first two mental health center staff members got permission from the board to defer all clinical work until December 1, 1959. During the fall, they talked with available local professionals, obtained consultation from state personnel, tried to recruit a psychiatrist, worked with the board, and prepared for a meeting in each county with representatives of all the local mental health influencing resources.

These county meetings were designed to produce a clearer picture of how professionals in each county viewed mental health problems, what solutions had been found, and what local professionals hoped the new mental health center might do to help them. The meetings were also designed to provide more professional contacts for mental health center staff members and to demonstrate something of the transactional patterns in each county. In these meetings, center staff members became better identified as they answered questions and explained their proposals for operation of the center. It was abundantly clear that everyone was waiting for the center to begin clinical work.

Transcripts of the taped proceedings of each county meeting were carefully prepared and sent to each participant and other presumably interested persons with the hope that this information could lead to more deliberate study of local problems. Whether or not these meetings served as anything more than early stepping-stones is uncertain. They were rarely mentioned again by anyone except center staff members who sometimes were reminded of places where their footing had slipped. One such misstep occurred when the school superintendent, who had been one of the three original promoters of the community mental health program, was too brusquely told that the center psychologist would not do routine psychological testing for the schools. Five years elapsed before the wound healed and reasonable mutual trust was established. Not soon enough had it been learned that when negative answers were required, it was far more politic and productive to look for positive alternatives than to try to back up a bald-faced "no" with sufficient evidence and logic to defeat the issue. We had to remember that we were negotiating long-term working relationships, not trying to win cases in court. Most of all, we had to remember that we were starting as outsiders and that our immediate and ever-continuing objective was to find opportunities to join the insiders with the hope that together all of us could develop more task-directed capability. From the beginning, such opportunities have become most available when we have been identified as willing to learn how to engage as co-professionals in various kinds of transactional settings. The subsequent metamorphosis of identity and engagement has been described in previous publications (Kiesler, 1965a, 1965b, 1967a, 1967b).

In two of the counties in our area, key professional people made certain that we were introduced to other key people in ways that fostered growth of effective collaborative working relationships with resource people of all kinds. In baffling contrast was our early experience in the other county. Initially, when the first two center staff members made contact with the welfare department in that county, they were informed that only a psychiatrist would be acceptable as a consultant. They found, too, that all of the other professionals in that county were polite but distant. School officials flatly stated that there were no problems they wished to discuss with anyone.

After I began full-time work as psychiatrist in July, 1960, one of my first professional callers was the director of the Welfare Department of that county. He invited me to visit him and suggested it might become possible to arrange regular consultative sessions with members of his staff and participation in an inservice training program. Since this was exactly what I had hoped for as a starting point, I accepted. Only weeks later did I find out how thoroughly I had been taken into captivity. How completely my contacts (or lack of them) with other professionals in that county had been managed did not become evident until after one of the doctors telephoned to ask if interested doctors could sit in on the training sessions planned for the welfare caseworkers. Because my first individual contacts with the doctors in that county had resulted only in exchanges of pleasantries, I had been waiting for some such indication of readiness for direct professional engagement. Pleased to be called, and responding to what I took to be my cue to go to work with them, I suggested meeting with the doctors as a group and was invited to the next hospital medical staff meeting. I thought this might be a real breakthrough.[5]

The evening of the meeting I arrived early. I was surprised to find that the first person at the hospital was the welfare director. During the meeting there was talk of how we might work together. I remarked that I would be glad to respond to the doctors' requests for consultation and that after I had had a chance to discuss cases with them we could accept referrals for direct evaluation and possible treatment at the center. One of the doctors questioned this, asking,

[5]Here, again, was a contrasting experience. As soon as I moved to Grand Rapids, doctors in the other two counties had immediately asked me to apply for active membership on the medical staffs of the local hospitals. In the third county, no similar suggestion came; and mention of my staff memberships in the other two counties had evoked not so much as an invitation to visit a hospital staff meeting. Eight years later, with relationships with individual doctors in good order, the possibility that I might apply for membership on their hospital staff has not yet been raised.

"Don't all of our patients have to go through the Welfare Department first?" Puzzled, I answered, "No, you can call on us directly." Looking around, I became aware of a stiffness in the room and an exchange of glances between the doctors and the welfare director. The meeting soon ended.

Subsequently, there were no direct requests from doctors. Occasionally, in the course of consulting with welfare caseworkers, it appeared necessary to involve one of the doctors. Upon calling on them at their offices, I found them still friendly but also still professionally aloof. The fact that three of them had known me previously only added to my confusion. One was a medical school classmate, and two had been students when I taught full time at the medical school. Months later I finally realized that the doctors had been led to believe that, because I was an employee of a government-affiliated agency, I properly should do business with only another government agency—the Welfare Department. In an attempt to correct what I assumed was a misunderstanding, I talked with the welfare director. When it became clear that it was not a misunderstanding, I acknowledged that without his help the county was literally closed to mental health center personnel. I went on to describe the valuable help the welfare directors in the other two counties had provided in suggesting contacts, making introductions, and helping to communicate a total community program concept. The welfare director's answer was blunt. "If you want to meet people here," he advised, "you'll have to do it on your own. I'm not here to make contacts for you. I've got my own department to develop."

We were kept sequestered in this way until after the welfare director left for another job. Meanwhile, we found that he did not deserve all of the credit for keeping us outsiders with only restricted entry visas. For example, it was only a year ago, after retirement of the former school superintendent, that we were first asked to supply scheduled consultative services to the schools. We knew that aggressive attempts to insert ourselves in that county's business would have been worse than futile. Repeatedly, we had to remind ourselves that we were so thoroughly engaged in the other two counties that we could afford to practice the art of the possible and wait for opportunities in the third county. Fortunately, the county commissioners of that county knew and understood the problem. They continued to appropriate their annual shares of support funds and to wait for opportunities of their own to encourage local resources to participate more fully in the area mental health program.

Early Success and Near Disaster

The test of the hypothesis that local primary professionals would try to use the center only as a place to which to send people, until they found at least equivalent value in other kinds of center professional services, came after clinical work began on December 1, 1959. By then a waiting list was already long. Despite the efforts of the staff to move cases as rapidly as possible, the waiting list persisted. It persisted until a deliberate attempt was made in the spring of 1960 to engage each referring professional at the moment a referral was received from him. The immediate objective was to estimate whether or not anything would really be added to diagnostic clarity or therapeutic results by direct service at the center. The long-range objective was development of inter-professional working relationships that could lead to more adequate handling of the clinical task by everyone.

Immediate engagement of referring professionals, instead of the people they referred, provided the opportunity to ask questions about the case at hand, about experience with other similar cases, about the professional's work, and about the community. When primary professionals found us sincerely interested in becoming better informed, they were usually actively helpful. In the course of these discussions, it frequently became evident that we could offer no more at the center than the primary professional was already providing. Often discussion enabled the primary professional to sort his thinking and to consider additional things he might do. When we demonstrated that we would try to be available at all times for interprofessional consultation, it soon became more common for primary professionals to ask us to confer about cases than to accept them. The result was that by the fall of 1960 seven out of ten cases discussed with primary professionals were retained by them, and our waiting list had permanently disappeared. Thereafter, we allocated only 20% of our collective professional time to direct clinical service activities.

Although the overall result demonstrated our expectation that primary professionals could switch from only referring people to making major use of consultative assistance, not all primary professionals made the switch and some did not even refer. After more than eight years, four medical practitioners continue to prefer nonengagement. The patients of two of them call us for appointments or come to the office, saying that the doctor told them to see us. When we call to find out the nature of their patients' problems, both doctors are cordial and give helpful information, but make it quite clear that they think more will be accomplished if we interact with their patients instead of with them. The other two view us with the same distaste as they do chiropractors. One has actively condemned us. He has said that he could not possibly trust us with medical information because two members of the center staff are nonmedical professionals. The fact that we are salaried, quasi-governmental employees also seems to make us suspect.

Initial success in establishing active collaborative relationships with most primary professionals carried no guarantee of permanence. We found we could not assume that these relationships would continue to be productive without repetitive re-seeding, cultivation, and pruning. Professionals new to the area, particularly because of normal personnel turnover in schools, the ministry, social agencies, and law enforcement, make relationship development a continuous process. Many professionals show persistent ambivalence toward various aspects of their mental health work and especially toward working with us on the terms we consider necessary. Unless we deliberately hold the line and concentrate on making their mental health work as rewarding as possible, they readily revert to simple referring roles.

That ambivalence is always present and that failure to take it into account may lead mental health professionals blindly into disaster is illustrated in an early attempt to obtain better quarters for the mental health center. In the fall of 1962, we found that if a public health services building, designed to house the mental health center, the county nursing service, a regional state department of health laboratory, and a sanitarian, could be attached to the Grand Rapids Hospital, Hill-Burton money would be available. Quickly checking, we also found that the local share of needed funds could be raised. There was room on the hospital grounds for such an addition.

Enthusiastically, the chairman of the mental health board, a general medical practitioner and part-time county public health officer, and I developed a proposal. We proposed to the hospital board that the mental health board provide all necessary building funds, that the public health services addition become entirely the property of the hospital under the direction of the hospital board, and that the mental health board pay rent to the hospital for the space occupied by the mental health center. The hospital board was actively interested. We were asked to come to a second meeting a week later. On our return, we were greeted with polite coolness. The chairman of the hospital board acknowledged our presence and then wasted no time in dismissing us by saying simply, "I'm sorry, gentlemen, the answer is no." And, by the tone of his voice, we knew unquestionably that the subject was closed.

Later that afternoon, we found someone who was willing to tell us what had happened. As doctors, and active members of the hospital medical staff, our board chairman and I had made the crucial mistake of not having officially cleared our proposal through medical staff channels before bringing it to the hospital board. Unthinkingly, we had naively assumed that our judgment would both be trusted and applauded by our medical colleagues. To our horror, we belatedly discovered that by-passing the medical staff had been regarded not only as a punishable breach of protocol (and a chance for retaliatory expression of protest against my insistence on certain items of protocol in my dealings with them) but also as a possible deliberate attempt to slip past the medical staff, into this exclusively private practice hospital, the opening wedge of government medicine.

Abruptly, we found we had opened a Pandora's box of ambivalence. All of the reservations, all of the fears, all of the dissatisfactions, all of the protest, all of the communications deficits and distortions had been mobilized. The grapevine had it that most of the doctors thought the mental health program was of little value and that the community could get along without it. It even appeared possible that the medical profession, including our board chairman, might close ranks, leaving me on the outside. Worse yet, because this eruption had been set off only two weeks before the county commissioners were to consider our annual request for funds to operate the area mental health program, we were confronted with a double-barrelled emergency.

Desperately in need of counsel, I called a general practitioner whose judgment I highly respected and whose candor I valued. I believed he had similar feelings toward me. He was also a member of the hospital medical staff executive committee. He knew the problem thoroughly. From the first, his own ambivalence had been in the open. When I came to Grand Rapids, he told me that he didn't like psychiatry and that he hoped I could relieve him of it. Later, although he continued to say the same thing, he added that as long as I was not going to relieve him of psychiatry, he had decided to learn to do it well. Even later, despite his still expressed wish to use his time for things in which he was more interested, he confessed that he had begun to like some aspects of his psychiatric work.

When I called late that Friday afternoon to ask him for help in figuring out what to do, he was quick to answer, "You sure do need help!" Since the next day was Saturday, we decided to meet after lunch for perhaps an hour or so. It took us five hours. Among the decisions we reached was the need for me to be invited to the hospital medical staff executive committee meeting on Monday morning so that I could ask the whole executive committee for advice. When I appeared, I assured the members of the executive committee that the building issue was entirely dead and that my only concern was eliminating misunderstandings and getting back on a solid working basis with everyone. They suggested we go through the same process with the whole staff at the regular meeting that Wednesday. We did.

The best proof that solutions were evolved, other than the fact that five years later we are still in business, is that the chief of the medical staff appeared before the county commissioners a week later to report that the doctors valued the help the mental health center gave them and their patients and that he thought the increased funds we needed should be appropriated. He held to this position even after the representative of the taxpayers' association heatedly questioned his truthfulness and insisted that one doctor had told him that all of the doctors were against the mental health center. The appropriation passed as requested.

In addition, there was an unexpected dividend. I was able, then and there, to seize the opportunity to invite the taxpayers' association representative to inspect the mental health center quarters and ask questions about the program. He accepted, and we talked so long we both missed lunch. Thereafter, I kept him regularly informed of our fiscal needs. He has not regarded them as unreasonable. Our gentlemen's understanding is that, as the taxpayers' association representative, he cannot be expected overtly to support anything that will raise taxes. He can only be unopposed.

In the years since 1960, while emphasizing diffusion of direct clinical service capability throughout the mental health influencing resources of the community, we have continued to deliver a small amount of direct specialty service. When consultation suggests that we can add something by direct evaluation, we invite the whole family to come. To avoid becoming tied down by a small number of inordinately time-consuming patients, we have used only brief, limited goal therapy.

When we see people for direct service, the principal objective is to put primary professionals into a better position to continue care locally. As often as possible, primary professionals are present and actively participate in our direct service work with the people for whom they are responsible. In that sense, we never have patients of our own; we are always facilitators. We also sit in with local professionals while they work on their own premises. When people require hospitalization for psychiatric help, they are usually admitted to local hospitals by their family doctors. We assist when asked to do so. We are also available to help with emergencies. Our local hospitals have no psychiatric beds. Patients with psychiatric problems are managed on medicine, surgery, obstetrics, pediatrics, and in the intensive care unit. If explicitly organized inpatient psychiatric facilities or programs should be needed, patients must still be referred to appropriate private or public hospitals outside of our area. When a psychiatrist undertakes a private practice in our area, transfer to other hospitals will be needed less often. Development of local extended care units may provide more local inpatient and partial hospitalization flexibility for many psychiatric patients. Because of the large size of this area and the relative diffusion of its small population, we have agreed that it will be impractical to develop a centralized mental health facility. Instead of trying to qualify for federal mental health construction and staffing funds, we will continue to emphasize local improvisation to provide the needed spectrum of essential services through existing resources and personnel in each population center in this area. Psychiatric units would be inappropriate and unwieldy in our small hospitals. The development of a process of treatment appears more suitable than the building and staffing of places for treatment.

From the beginning, interactions with other professionals about specific clinical cases have been regarded as the major educational route to increased mental health problem-solving capability for professionals of all kinds, including the three members of the center staff. With growing acquaintance and mutual confidence, recognition of the informal educational impact of case consultation led early to requests for help in devising and conducting many kinds of formal instructional sessions. Groups of professionals wishing to update their knowledge and skills have involved us in everything from presenting isolated lectures to conducting regularly scheduled permanent staff development seminars. In short order, also, opportunities to assist school and welfare administrators and civic groups in their efforts to solve administrative or programmatic problems affecting whole population segments took us beyond the clinical task and opened the door to work on both the primary preventive task and the measurement task (Kiesler, 1968; Stennett, 1967; Stennett & Bounds, 1966).

Board Responsibilities

After professional staff members had been employed and had begun to establish the interprofessional working relationships necessary to community-wide program development, the mental health board functioned as little more than a clearinghouse for staff proposals and the overseer of fiscal affairs. From time to time, individual board members acted as spokesmen or program promoters in their own counties. Otherwise, program evolution became essentially a staff operation while the board receded into the background. Partly responsible was the size of the area. Board members from different counties, and sometimes from the same county, seldom encountered one another between board meetings. For the same reason, committees could not function unless they consisted entirely of board members from one county or unless they met briefly in conjunction with board meetings. Usually chairmen did the necessary work and then asked their committees to review it before recommendations were brought to the board. Neither the board nor its committees actually generated proposals. They became almost entirely responsive to staff stimulation.

In contrast, we three professional staff members became increasingly visible as we systematically traveled to all parts of the area and enthusiastically worked toward the establishment of regularly scheduled contacts with local resources. As often as possible, our initial contacts were made by at least two, and often all three, of us working together. We wanted to make more than one of us visible to each resource and wanted to give each of us active experience with each resource. Of the several objectives of this kind of multiple exposure, the most important was the opportunity for any one of the three of us to emerge eventually as the principal interactor with any resource. Although some relationships were professionally pre-ordained, such as mine with medical resources, most relationships evolved irrespective of our professional disciplines. All three of us have continued to interact with most resources, sometimes interchangeably and sometimes for special purposes. In consequence, we have placed ourselves in a unique position. Among all of the professionals in the community, we are the only ones whose normal business provides active transactional contact with all other community resources.

However, even with full authority from the board and success in establishing professional-to-professional (and administrator-to-administrator) relationships, we found that staff members could not effectively handle some kinds of transactions. As program administrator, I at first tried to act for the board in all transactions with other boards. It is easy now, in retrospect, to say that I should not have been so willing to carry the ball. At the time, however, I was not only too willing but also so eager to become involved in every aspect of program operation that I failed to understand some of the rules of the game. My willingness to get involved also contributed to the passivity of the board during the first years.

One annual responsibility of the program director is preparation of a budget and financing plan for each ensuing year. After approval by the mental health board, each Board of County Commissioners is requested to agree to provide a specific amount of financial support.[6] In the beginning, these requests for support went out over my signature, and I was invited to appear before the county boards to answer questions. My first appearance before the Itasca County Board was pleasant, and the agreement was unanimously approved. The next year it was necessary to ask for a modest increase in support. Anticipating another friendly reception, I came early to the Itasca County Board meeting to find the commissioners listening to the polished pitch of a road grader blade salesman. Stimulated by his performance and the favorable response of the board, I began to answer the first question about progress of our program with a glowing description of all of the interesting things we had accomplished during the year. Abruptly, one board member interrupted. "We don't care about all that," he said, "How many have ya cured?" I tried to explain that a simple answer was not possible because we were seeing relatively few patients ourselves and concentrating major efforts on trying to help others to deliver diagnostic and treatment services. Moreover, because the program included many more things than patient treatment, I said that results had to be stated in many more dimensions than number of "cures." He repeated his question. When I went on to say that we were trying to devise ways to measure the influence of multiple factors, including our own efforts, on treatment outcomes, it satisfied him even less. Not knowing how to proceed, I was relieved and grateful when another board member interjected, "This seems to be a more complicated matter than we perhaps realize. It may not be possible to talk about the cost of a cure in the same way that we talk about the cost of a piece of equipment for road maintenance." He then moved approval of the agreement, and it was unanimously passed.

When I came the following year to the county board meeting, I was well armed with charts and graphs designed to show what Itasca County's money had bought. The commissioners were polite but took little time to listen to explanations. There were pointed comments about "mushrooming costs" and the need to hold the line on taxes; but, again, the appropriation was approved. Because the county attorney had been at the meeting, I found him later in his office and asked him what was happening. He didn't mince words. "You're the wrong one to answer these questions. You may think you represent the public's interest in mental health, but they see you as a salesman working for a big

[6]Basically corresponding to each county's share of the population of the area.

commission for yourself." Thereafter, the chairman of the mental health board (which really represents the public) made all requests for funds; and I made no more money-raising appearances before county boards.

Full comprehension of the strategic position of the board lagged until three years ago. While the language of the 1957 legislation clearly gave each community mental health board general responsibility for mental health and mental retardation program development in its area, it conveyed no authority for anything but facility operation. Mental health boards were slow to recognize that, although they had no authority over other organizations or agencies concerned with mental health and mental retardation, the 1957 legislation had charged them with fostering coordination and enhancement of many kinds of efforts throughout the community. Even then, it was initially assumed by all of us that these responsibilities could be delegated to professional employees of the board.

When the Northland Mental Health Board finally began to explore the full range of its responsibilities, the mental health center had come into perspective as a professional service organization having a spectrum of patient-oriented and population-oriented functions addressed principally to the clinical task. The board had also created a separate research organization[7] to take responsibility for work on the population-oriented measurement task. Preliminary plotting of suggested routes toward work on the primary preventive task was underway. The board was ready to move beyond facility operation into a community process approach of its own.

Seeking first to inform itself of where and how it might assist, the board met with representatives of schools, law enforcement agencies, and welfare. An almost immediate result of meeting with welfare board members was the opportunity to put into action our basic policy that our own professional staff should always remain small and highly mobile and that service gaps can be filled best by increasing the capabilities of local primary service structures. The specific opportunity for demonstration of this policy stemmed from the fact that Minnesota law provides that each county welfare board shall be responsible for the adequacy of local planning for the care of all persons from that county who receive care in any of the state's mental health or mental retardation facilities. Metropolitan county welfare departments have long had mental health units, but there had been no mental health workers in rural county welfare departments. Stimulated by local data showing the numbers of people in need of more organized local services, the Itasca County Welfare Board and the Northland Mental Health Board jointly obtained funds to create in the Itasca County Welfare Department a new mental health worker position. Consequently, the mental health work of the welfare department has been better organized and

[7]The Social Science Research Program, established in 1961, operates parallel to the mental health center and is entirely supported by research grants.

more productive. The mental health board has made similar efforts to assist schools to obtain social workers and psychologists.

Another opportunity for the mental health board to emerge with community relationships and functions of its own was presented when the Minnesota Legislature passed a new Hospitalization and Commitment Act[8] in 1967. The Northland Mental Health Board conducted information sessions in each county for medical practitioners, hospital and nursing home administrators and nursing supervisors, welfare caseworkers, county nurses, sheriffs, policemen, judges, attorneys, and others. Not only did all of these professionals in each county need to become accurately informed of the provisions of the new act but, most importantly, they also needed to be brought into the same room together long enough to confront one another with their questions and to begin the process of negotiating local ground rules for implementation of the act.

Personnel and the Adaptive Process

Rural community mental health programs are always in danger of striking out in competition with metropolitan areas for professional manpower. Long parochial gestation in standard residencies and graduate training programs produces professional littermates accustomed to huddling together in university cities. Eloquently testifying to the metropolitan nurture, not only of those who design them but also of those who can be recruited to staff them, are practically all of the "Federal type" comprehensive community mental health centers currently in operation or in planning. Even if modified formulas and criteria were to make large rural areas with relatively low population concentrations eligible for Federal construction and staffing grants, recruiting would still be difficult. Beyond the fact that there will never be enough mental health professionals to fill all of the job openings is the even more limiting fact that the preferences of most mental health personnel for urban settings are exceeded only by those of their spouses.

Nevertheless, rural programs attract professionals and often keep them amazingly well. Higher salaries and more generous personnel policies may be required, particularly in areas distant from large cities. To prevent professional isolation and stagnation, rural community mental health boards must expect their professional employees to participate actively in local, regional, and state professional organizations and to attend at least one national professional meeting each year. It is essential that expenses be paid entirely by the program so that cost cannot be used as an excuse for nonattendance.

The mobility and community involvement required of mental health professionals in population-oriented programs produce far more exposure than most of us have previously experienced. When we began work in our area, we knew

[8]Minnesota Statutes, 1967, Section 253 A.01 to 253 A.21.

that the pattern of operation we proposed would mean daily exposure of our professional activities to the scrutiny and judgment (and criticism) of other professionals. Therefore, we decided to make maximum use of exposure to achieve two objectives. One was comfortable reciprocal candor in our relationships with other professionals. In order to expect others to invite us into full participation, we concluded that we had to be willing to let them see every aspect of our work. This we have done. There is no professional situation that cannot include another legitimately connected professional. Our other objective was demonstrating that we could learn from one another to the extent that our work and their work are parts of the same continua of knowledge and skills. Deliberately, we have used full exposure of our work to dispel any lingering assumptions that "real" mental health work consists of esoteric rites conducted in inner sancta by peculiar professionals with magic powers.

Rural areas offer no hiding places. The personal and family detachment and relative anonymity so often cherished and readily maintained by mental health professionals in metropolitan areas are neither possible nor desirable. With high visibility inevitable, we found it necessary to be accurately identified. As professionals, we could immediately be trusted to perform certain technical functions. As people, we had to earn trust.

For example, we had to demonstrate that we did not take tales home from the office. Very quickly we learned how to handle repeated situations in which people we had seen in the office one day were introduced to us and to our wives and children in social or business settings the next day. When it was evident that we could comfortably take appropriate social or business roles under those circumstances and that members of our families were unaware of any other connection with us, everyone proceeded without difficulty. Anticipating such situations, each of us had previously reached an understanding with his family that if any persons to whom family members were introduced appeared already to know us, family members were never to ask about the circumstances of the prior acquaintance. The rule has worked. Every day members of our families associate unknowingly with people who are, or who have been, our patients.

Until the community could become sufficiently sure of our personal labels, we could not expect our professional functions to include participation in community process. Not only our personal attributes but also our interests, our life styles, our drinking habits, our marriages, our children, our religious practices, our politics, and our positions on various issues of current concern had to be cataloged before we could become personally predictable enough to be trusted with more than technical professional questions. Only when professionals have lived in rural areas long enough to emerge as citizens with as much personal stake in the future of the community as anyone else can their communities begin to make full use of their capabilities in mental health program development.

References

Kiesler, F. Is this psychiatry? In S. E. Goldston (Ed.), *Concepts of community psychiatry.* PHS Publication No. 1319. Washington, D.C.: U.S. Government Printing Office, 1965. Pp. 147–157.(a)

Kiesler, F. Programming for prevention. *North Carolina Journal of Mental Health,* 1965, *1* (2), 3–17.(b)

Kiesler, F. Contribution to general discussion. In R. R. Monroe, G. D. Klee, & E. B. Brody (Eds.), *Psychiatric epidemiology and mental health planning.* Research Report No. 22, Washington, D.C.: American Psychiatric Association 1967. Pp. 361–362.(a)

Kiesler, F. Is psychiatry enough? *McCormick Quarterly,* July, 1967, *21* 55–68 (Special issue).(b)

Kiesler, F. Building an event-reporting system. In R. H. Williams & L. D. Ozarin (Eds.), *Community mental health: An international perspective.* San Francisco: Jossey-Bass, 1968. Pp. 284–291.

Stennett, R. G. Control in educational programming: Concept, vehicle, case in point. *Elementary School Journal,* 1967, *67,* 317–322.

Stennett, R. G., & Bounds, T. D. Premarital pregnancy and marital stability. *The Social Worker (Le Travailleur Social),* 1966, *34* (3), 142–148.

Chapter 7
A Mental Health Program for
the Urban Multiservice Center

Harris B. Peck and Seymour R. Kaplan

The history of health care in the United States has gone through many phases. Initially, the aim was to set up autonomous agencies of high quality that would serve the separate health needs of the individual. As these developed, not only was there fragmentation between different health areas, but there was little coordination between agencies in one specific health area. Recent Federal legislation, especially in mental health, has required the development of a plan of service that evolves from a critical review of all the services in the community available to meet specific health problems. As a result, interagency planning committees developed which led to greater coordination of the services within the given specialty. As we have become more and more aware of the multiple health problems individuals have that require the services of many specialists, as well as the interrelationship between the various disciplines, the trend for comprehensive centers that include all health and welfare facilities has developed. In these, mental health facilities form only one aspect. This view has recently been incorporated in a Federal program for the model cities. How the mental health specialist can participate in such a new program and what problems arise is the focus of Dr. Peck and Dr. Kaplan's chapter.

Chapter 7

A Mental Health Program for the Urban Multiservice Center

Harris B. Peck and Seymour R. Kaplan

Paradoxically the American central city during the past several decades has been thrust out to the periphery of our urban life and national awareness. The force of the recent disturbances in our cities attests to the years of neglect and the psychosocial displacement of large numbers of our fellow citizens. Although those most critically disadvantaged may as yet only represent a minority of city dwellers, the ultimate effect of these conditions already threatens to seriously damage and impair the quality of urban life for all. Hopefully, current efforts at intervention, such as those embodied in the Model Cities program, while primarily mobilizing Federal and local resources for the benefit of lower economic neighborhoods, carry a promise of better days for the American city as a whole.

Such a mobilization is long overdue in the design and operation of mental health services for the disadvantaged urban community. Generally these services have been among the least adequate, most deficient, and least integrated into the overall range of human services required for the maintenance of life and the preservation of physical and psychosocial well-being.

The primary organizational form developed thus far by the Model Cities program for the lower socioeconomic community is the Neighborhood Multiservice Center. The National Institute of Mental Health is presently encouraging the organization of community mental health centers for the delivery of psychiatric and mental health services. The National Institute of Mental Health is an agency within the Department of Health, Education, and Welfare, one of the Federal partners in the Model Cities program which includes the Office of Economic Opportunity, Department of Labor, and the Department of Housing and Urban Development. Since the organization of a mental health center involves functions that extend beyond the formal boundaries of psychiatry, it almost inevitably encroaches on the province of each of these great Federal departments. The Multiservice Center minimally can reduce duplication and fragmentation. Potentially it provides an exciting organizational vehicle through which the urban community mental health center can effectively relate to the diverse functions and services critical to the achievement of mental health objectives. Such collaboration at a time when both community mental health centers and multiservice centers are still in the planning stages may exert a significant influence on the directions taken by both types of programs.

In the presentation that follows we will try to illustrate and make concrete certain of these general considerations by drawing on the experience of the Lincoln Hospital Mental Health Services—Albert Einstein College of Medicine, which is presently developing a comprehensive community mental health center in conjunction with the Model Cities Hunts Point Multiservice Center in the South Bronx.

Prior to the organization of the Lincoln Hospital Mental Health Services in the latter part of 1963, there were almost literally no formal psychiatric or mental health services operating within Hunts Point, and there were none for the entire South Bronx region, which comprises a population of more than 350,000 people.

Needless to say, this dearth of facilities does not reflect any lack of need in an area referred to in a study by the Institute of Public Administration (Logue, 1966) in the following terms:

> "The most troubled portions of New York are its three major slum and blighted areas—Harlem, South Bronx, and Central Brooklyn . . . These three areas have the highest incidence of poverty-stricken families and welfare and the greatest sense of alienation . . . the highest incidence of unemployment in the city and the most severe social problems."

Indeed, in almost every imaginable category that reflects the extent of psychosocial pathology, this community compares poorly to either the Bronx as a whole or to all of New York City.

Admissions to State Civil Mental Hospitals. There were 52% more admissions during the year ending March, 1965, than during the year ending March, 1961. The rate of admissions was 3.0 per 1,000 persons, 33.3% higher than the rate in the Bronx and 30.4% higher than that of New York. However, admissions to state civil mental hospitals probably do not directly reflect the incidence of psychiatric pathology in the community, since the psychiatric services have been deficient and poorly adapted to low-income groups, who are poorly informed about services that are available and often decline to utilize those that exist.

Homicides and Suicides. The number of homicides in the area increased 29% between 1960 and 1965. Suicides in 1965 were 44% higher than they had been in 1960.

Education. In 1960 median school years completed for the population 25 years and over ranged from 8.4 to 8.6, compared to 10.1 for New York City. The unfortunate truth that another generation will bear the scars of the ghetto is suggested by an analysis of reading scores of 583 eighth-grade students in October, 1965, by the New York City Board of Education. It showed that 19.7% were four to five years behind in reading, an additional 21.3% were three to four years behind, and 18.7% were two to three years behind. Thus, almost

60% of the students were more than two years behind in reading. In total, 81.1% of the students did not read at the level they were expected to reach.

Juvenile Delinquency. In 1961 juvenile delinquency offenses for the area were 1,492; by 1965 they had risen to 1,929—a 29.3% increase. In 1964 the rate of juvenile delinquency per 1,000 youths between the ages of seven and 20 was 92.1 compared to 47.9 for New York City. Out-of-wedlock births increased between 1962 and 1965.

Venereal Disease. The venereal disease rate per 100,000 youths under 21 was 374.4 in 1964, compared to 211.3 in the whole Bronx. Total venereal disease cases reported in 1960 and 1965 showed a 234.6% increase in gonorrhea and 28.8% increase in syphilis over the five-year period.

Infant Mortality; Prenatal Care. The 1965 rate of infant mortality per 1,000 live births was 31.2, compared to 25.7 for the Bronx and 25.8 for New York City. In the same year, the percentage of live births having later prenatal care (after six months) or no care at all was 41.1%, 55% higher than the figures for the Bronx and 73% higher than those for New York City.

Divorce or Separation. In 1960, 8.3% of the population 14 years and over were divorced or separated, compared to 5.8% for the Bronx as a whole.

Welfare. In April, 1965, with 1960 population figures as the base, 18% of the area's population—almost one of every five persons—were on welfare. This compares to 6% for New York City. Seventy percent of the recipients were in the fatherless ADC (Aid for Dependent Children) category in April, 1966.

Unemployment. The unemployed represented 8.3% of the total labor force (people over 14) in 1960, compared to 5.2% for the Bronx and New York City.

Income. In 1960, of the 22,540 families residing in the area, 26.8% had yearly incomes of less than $3,000 and an additional 17.6% had incomes between $3,000 and $4,000.

Housing. The 1960 census figures show that of 26,652 housing units in the area, 95.4% (24,425) were built before 1939 and most of those before 1920. Neglect of these old buildings, compounded by overcrowding, has led to further deterioration of housing. More than one-third (34.8%) of all housing units in the area were classified "deteriorated" or "dilapidated" by the 1960 census.

From this brief summary of the demographic data, it requires little imagination to recognize that this is a community in crisis. A partial reflection of these critical conditions is seen in the cases of severely disturbed individuals and families that appear in the Lincoln Hospital Emergency Room, on the medical wards, and in the desperate and often hopeless attempts at referral by the various public and voluntary agencies. For every such case it is evident that there are many more unrecognized instances of severe untreated psychopathology. Equally tragic is the host of neglected opportunities to intervene and prevent disaster in the face of clearly defined mental health hazards. When the Lincoln Hospital Mental Health Services was established as a medically based institution created by a contract between the city of New York and the Albert Einstein College of Medicine, it seemed evident that its initial responsibility was to meet the most urgent, critical, and immediate needs for direct psychiatric services.

How to proceed from that point was far more difficult to determine. The Federal legislation providing for comprehensive community mental health centers (much less its local implementation) was as yet some years away. No adequate theoretical framework, overall strategy, or system of technique was generally available.

The approach that finally emerged reflected some years of prior experimentation within the Division of Social and Community Psychiatry of the Albert Einstein College of Medicine.[1] In the course of our work with families, small groups, and the ward milieu of a day hospital, we had been impressed by the possibility of substantially altering the adaptation of the individual through intervention directed at one or another of these aspects of the social milieu (Peck, 1963). It was but a short step to the assumption around which much of the Lincoln program was developed, namely that *there is an intimate relationship between the social organization of the community and the psychological organization of its residents.*

Indeed the enormous deprivation, high degree of psychosocial pathology, and scarcity of resources within the area might well lead one to the question whether any strategy could have significant impact unless it were oriented toward the broadest kind of social change compatible with the overall mental health mandate.[2] Although initially we foresaw some benefit accruing from attempts to bring together the existing agency programs in a more integrated fashion, the overburdened public and private agencies in the area soon made known their own severe limitations, helplessness, and discouragement in the face of overwhelming tasks confronting them. As for the citizens of the South Bronx, although there was evidence that some groups and organizations were pressing for improvements in conditions and services, they appeared to have made relatively minimal inroads on the major problems of the area. The general population at first glance seemed either uninvolved or apathetic. Nevertheless, despite, or perhaps because of, these obstacles, it appeared that the achievement of any major mental health objectives in the community would require substantial alterations both inside and outside the formal agency and institutional structure. Needless to say, the task of delineating an appropriate role for a public mental health organization within these two spheres of action is complicated, delicate, and difficult. Most programs tend to address themselves to one or another of

[1]Supported as the Center for Small Group and Family Research by the National Institute of Mental Health, Grant No. MH 1132–1.
[2]Materials in the following section of this presentation are drawn largely from the paper by Struening and Peck (1968).

two basic approaches, i.e., from the institution "down" or from the people "up." We wondered if it might be possible to develop a coordinated strategy, combining an emphasis on institutional consultation and training programs with some way of implementing and facilitating those processes of social change and social action around which the community grows and develops and from which positive mental health objectives might accrue (Peck, Kaplan, & Roman, 1966).

We recognized at the outset that our goals would tend to be substantially influenced by our own interests, competences, biases, and identities. Out of this awareness we attempted to organize ourselves into a flexible structure that would enable us to continue to learn and respond to what we hoped would be an ever-growing knowledge of the community and its needs. We tried to make some determination of such needs from the available demographic data and through exchange of information and the establishment of consultative relationships with the departments of the hospital and the various public and private agencies in the community.

The Hospital and the Community

We viewed our initial program effort as one that combined the elements of a study and of a consultation program directed toward hospital departments and community agencies, focusing particularly on those small leadership groups to which we had access within these organizations. For the base-line study of Lincoln Hospital, a team of two interviewers used a structured, but open-ended, interview schedule and questioned at least two staff members from each of the major departments of the hospital. A similar approach was adapted to the more varied conditions of the community agencies. The interviews were designed to give qualitative and quantitative information on each department or agency's need for, and potential utilization of, mental health services. We also inquired into the internal structure and relationships to other departments and agencies. Analysis of the interviews provided an estimate of the future demands on the mental health services. Thus, we gained a birds-eye view of the major dynamic features of the hospital as a total operating unit and some sense of the overall agency configuration. The survey was also intended to serve as a reference for future planning and to provide a set of quantifiable data that could later be duplicated and compared with the early data.

It was evident from the outset that the needs for direct service by such departments as Medicine, Pediatrics, or Ob-Gyn or such agencies as the public schools could, if acceded to, swamp all of the available mental health staff resources with referred cases. This recognition led to the idea of a Multipurpose Clinical Facility initially designed as the primary instrument for relating to various departments of the hospital and the various public and voluntary community agencies. The rather cumbersome title (Multipurpose Clinical Facility) was chosen because it seemed an accurate description and because it served as a reminder that the functions of the facility are not primarily those of the usual psychiatric outpatient or mental hygiene clinic. The Multipurpose Clinical Facility provides information, referral, diagnostic, and consultative services. However, treatment contacts are mostly crisis oriented and are generally limited to about six individual or family interviews. All such contacts are viewed as opportunities to gain access to any one of the variety of subsystems of which the primary patient is a member and which may be in crisis (Peck & Kaplan, 1966). Thus, wherever feasible an attempt is made to investigate the individual's association with one or another aspect of his social milieu, which may bear on the difficulty that leads him to seek help.[3] In practice, this approach leads to the involvement of the total family in the evaluation and treatment, with particular attention to the welfare, housing, or other realistic social concerns that almost always accompany the psychological symptoms in the adult population we serve. Whether help to the individual patient requires assistance to a family in crisis or intervention into some critical aspect of the family's relation with a community agency, an attempt is made to address our efforts both to the individual in distress and to that aspect of the social system that appears to be associated with the difficulty.

Limitations of the Initial Organizational Structure

The organizational structure as outlined above was primarily designed to provide crisis-oriented services, collect data, engage in collaborative planning with hospital departments and community agencies, and to provide, expand, modify, and coordinate services through a program of consultation, training, and direct services. However, experience within our own city and others suggested that services developed along these lines alone would be far from adequate to meet the needs of an impoverished community like the South Bronx.

The public service agencies constitute, because of their fragmentation, complexity, and bureaucracy, a frustrating and seemingly insurmountable network of barriers. The voluntary family and children's agencies have only one office each to serve the entire Bronx (former neighborhood offices and outposts have been consolidated in the interest of economy). Each is located (as are many of the public agencies) in middle-class neighborhoods at considerable distance from those who need the service most. The traditional ways of operating—waiting lists, weekly appointments, long-term service, and emphasis on "talking through"—are not consonant with the needs, the experience, or the life style of low-income people for many reasons. The very complexity of

[3] The prototype for this approach has been described by Peck (1963) in work conducted in a psychiatric day hospital, which suggested that changes in the status of an individual necessitating institutional psychiatric care are accompanied by and related to a significant alteration or decompensation in some small group, such as the family, in which the patient is a nuclear interacting member.

the urban structure makes it difficult and frustrating for individuals (even those who are long-time residents) to know about and make proper use of resources. Unfamiliarity with the city and the intricacies of its various bureaucratic structures contribute to the sense of powerlessness, anomie, and helplessness of many as they attempt to deal with problems of employment, housing, education, recreation, income, etc. For reasons arising from differences in socialization and life experiences, low-income people are even less skilled than their middle-class counterparts in dealing with and using these services. In particular, they are less able to formulate their needs "acceptably," to state their complaints, or to assert their rights. Since low-income people require the concrete services of some of these systems for sheer survival, as well as for their social and psychological well-being, the inability to voice their needs effectively can be a major source of frustration, impotence, and reinforcement of self-defeating behavior.

The obstacles encountered by the low-income population in obtaining services from the formal agency structure will also be reflected in efforts to enlist the agencies' participation in planning more appropriate services. There are, to be sure, substantial difficulties in engaging the personnel of a school or welfare department to participate with a mental health agency in planning, modifying, and extending services. Nevertheless, there are various levels of communication and authority along which information can be exchanged, influence exerted, and some changes introduced.

No such lines extend from a mental health agency like the Lincoln Hospital Mental Health Services to the informal organizational structure of the South Bronx community. Although the structure is still largely unknown, we must not only assume that it exists but that it may in actuality have functions and dimensions that from the mental health point of view compare significantly to the formal agency structure. Early in our efforts to establish ourselves in the community, we made contact with such community agencies as the Association of Bronx Community Organizations, the South Bronx Community Council, the Puerto Rican Forum, United Neighborhood Houses, and a number of other community groups that could, if persuaded of our intentions, both give us relevant data about the South Bronx and engage in collaborative activities. Much later on, when our Research Division had been established, we did an intensive study of the religious denominations and sects in the area, and were able to begin to differentiate among their chosen social functions and the community's expectations of them. In some cases, we were able to develop collaborative or consultative mental health activities with some of the religious organizations. But all of these developments were gradual and slow. Nevertheless, we were faced with an interesting question that required immediate and ongoing exploration.

As one becomes acquainted with a deprived urban area like the South Bronx, the question is not why its statistics are so alarming but rather why they are not more so. How do so many of its residents maintain their sanity, self-esteem, and autonomy? Clearly this "disorganized" community must and does have its own unique informal organizational structure which is at least as effective in maintaining, "treating," and rehabilitating its citizens psychologically and socially as is the very limited and deficient formal agency structure. One of the tasks of the mental health agency is to learn about this informal network in the community, which so often is invisible to the "outsider." It is necessary to bring together "outside" and "inside" data, as well as resources and thus contribute to our knowledge and ability to coordinate them all in the interest of the community.

Thus, it was evident that an organizational structure as thus far described had a number of limitations.

1. It did not make adequate provision for integrating the so-called "mental health approach" with a social action approach. The former works within the agency structure through training, consultation, and direct services, while the latter may bring about major alterations in the operation and utilization of existing institutional services, develop new ones, and drastically alter the level of citizen participation and thus the apathy, powerlessness, and general psychosocial climate of the community.

2. Although some programs integrated certain of the hospital based clinical services with those of the public and private community agencies, there was no channel for connecting this formal organizational structure of the community with its great unutilized mental health potential. Without such connections it seemed unlikely that we would be able to close those gaps in vital services that are often the lethal chasms in which the lives and minds of the residents of a low-income area are lost.

3. Finally, it lacked a form that would keep us from falling into the very bureaucratic pitfalls that seemed to account for so many of the deficiencies in existing services.

a. Coordination and integration seem almost inevitably to lead to increasing organizational size, and thus contribute further to the development of impersonal, dehumanized services.

b. The more complex the organizational structure becomes, the more difficult it is for the people of the community to find points of entry into the systems where they can make their needs known and participate in its planning or operation.

Without such citizen participation and despite our best intentions, we might end by contributing further to the community's dependency and apathy rather than fostering the kind of autonomy that would ensure the continuity and development of programs that cannot depend on the professional community alone for their survival. It also seemed probable that without more direct and extensive access to the community the likelihood of enlisting its participation in any ultimate plan of intervention would be limited and ineffective.

The Neighborhood Service Center—Mental Health Aide Program

In February, 1965, we established a single, storefront "outpost" which we designated a Neighborhood Service Center. This Center was to serve as a base for service and community action programs and to help us become acquainted with the relatively alien world of the South Bronx. To staff the Center, we recruited residents of the neighborhood, some of whom had already been engaged in trying to help themselves and their neighbors deal with their problems, and others we thought had potential for doing so. In training them we tried to make some contribution to the competence and skills they already possessed. We also aspired to learn from them something of their knowledge about the community and the skill they had acquired in living and working within it.

When we opened this first Neighborhood Service Center, staffed with six nonprofessional mental health aides under the supervision of a mental health professional, we did not detail the functions or services the Center's staff would be engaged in. The staff, through their interaction with the residents of the neighborhood, was to explore the needs of the people and determine the ways in which we could or could not be helpful.

In establishing the Center without first setting up or making contact with some sort of community group, we might be accused of acting in direct contradiction to our own avowed philosophy. But, in fact, a number of circumstances made us decide to take this action without attempting first to develop community sanction for it. First, on a purely practical level, we had been given the demonstration grant to develop the Center; and we were reluctant to use three or four months of the grant period for the necessary planning and research that would be involved if we were to find or help establish sanctioning groups. Second, since our problem consisted of this very lack of knowledge, the Neighborhood Service Center seemed an eminently practical method of combining this sort of research with direct services to people badly in need of them.

We were not unduly naive. We certainly knew that there were many needs we were not prepared to meet. Some services might be extracted with difficulty from various public and voluntary agencies. Still others might require considerable creative innovation or even major alterations in the organizational and power structure of the community. Beginning in January, 1965, we began to receive support from the Community Action Program of the Office of Economic Opportunity, which enabled us to open two additional Neighborhood Service Centers and to train over 50 aides in all.

Our three Neighborhood Service Centers have become the settings in the community to which many residents turn in time of crisis. In this way, the Centers are able to keep abreast of the kinds of psychosocial problems with which the residents have to cope, the services needed, and their availability. Similarly, the gaps, limitations, and deficiencies are detected more readily in the formal service structure and informal arrangements currently employed by the community. As clients come in to request help with specific problems, the expediting mental health worker rapidly discovers, in the course of attempting to obtain the necessary services, when and where there are no provisions available for one or another kind of problem.

Thus, the Centers serve as important sources of information about the nature of the social changes needed, as well as potential foci from which action to implement the changes can arise. The initiation of programs varies not only according to the nature of the problem encountered, but also from one Center to the next in terms of differing priority of needs, relationships to the community, etc.

For example, our Center No. 1 has a smaller volume of walk-in clients than do the other two. It does, however, have a close contact with the community and has been particularly active in organizing the community around such issues as the closing of St. Francis (the only other inpatient hospital facility in the Lincoln Hospital area). Community action failed to stop this, but when a later crisis developed—around the city's failure to act on a crash program for the renovation of Lincoln Hospital for which funds had already been appropriated—Neighborhood Service Center No. 1 collaborated with the South Bronx Community Council in plans to bring pressure on the city. In this case, the response from the city departments involved in the delay was immediate; and the crash program will move ahead.

Center No. 2, on the other hand, gets more walk-in clients whose problems center around the administration of the Welfare Department than do the others. In addition, therefore, to direct intervention on behalf of these clients, this Center has been more successful in organizing welfare recipients to learn what their rights are and how to deal with the agencies than have the other Centers, although all three engage in these organizing activities.

Center No. 3 was handed the mandate, by Lincoln Hospital Mental Health Services, to work with patients discharged from Bronx State Hospital and provide a variety of aftercare services. But other activities in this Center stemmed directly from priorities selected by the community. Schools were demanding help with troublesome students and in getting indifferent parents to communicate more with the schools. Because this Center got so many clients with housing complaints, they organized successful Tenants' Councils to work on code enforcement and housing legislation.

These social action activities, although still limited in scope, are beginning to engage the population receiving service at the Centers in a graduated series of tasks of increasing complexity, as the activities just described indicate. The Centers have been involved in campaigning to register voters, in organizing block clean-up programs, in discussing complaints against Lincoln Hospital with community residents. In addition to protest activity, the Neighborhood Service Centers have been involved in a variety of collaborative activities with local institutions and agencies, such as welfare and housing organizations, as well as the schools already mentioned.

Consolidating the Demonstration

It is evident from the brief summary above that after only two or so years of the Neighborhood Service Center-Mental Health Aide program, the Lincoln Hospital Mental Health Services had begun to engage in functions, both in its case-by-case activities as well as in its community programs, that were not ordinarily associated with a mental health agency. Although these activities were begun primarily in the spirit of demonstration and exploration, several major developments are presently contributing to their consolidation into the ongoing program of the Lincoln Hospital Mental Health Services.

1. A major factor in this regard is the opportunity accorded by the establishment of the Model Cities Multiservice Center within the community.

2. A second consideration grows out of the need to delineate the specific shape and structure of the community mental health center as imposed by the formal requirements of the National Institute of Mental Health construction and staffing applications, in order to provide continuing "hard money" support for the community mental health center.

3. A third very significant pressure grows out of the necessity for substantial expansion of manpower development programs that emerged out of the initial recruitment and training of mental health aides from the community. The extension of this program has now been launched with the assistance of private foundation support for planning and pilot projects in a greatly broadened health careers program.

The three developments enumerated above have all tended to accelerate the consolidation of demonstration activities into an ongoing organizational structure for the Lincoln Hospital Mental Health Services. To counter the possibilities of prematurely freezing innovative and as yet incompletely studied aspects of the demonstration into a closed, rigid structure, an extensive program of research and evaluation has been established. This program includes substantial provision for monitoring the various components of the program and systematically feeding back the findings into administration, planning, and development. This emphasis on a continuing process of planning and development derives from a view of the mental health agency as a change agent engaged in a continuous dynamic interaction with the community and its various substructures. Thus, the design for the Model Cities Neighborhood Mental Health Unit incorporates an awareness of both the limitations and achievements of the demonstration as thus far developed. Within this context, research findings are to be utilized in an ongoing fashion so as to provide administration with guidelines for consolidation of the program as effectiveness is established and for making modifications as they become necessary.

Introducing Health and Mental Health Services into the Multiservice Center

The Hunts Point Multiservice Center, in accordance with the Federal guidelines for the Model Cities program, is sponsored by the representatives of the community it is to serve. All the various pertinent municipal agencies representing the major arms of the municipal government have obligated themselves to assist in providing a broad range of human services. These include:

1. The Human Resources Administration, which comprises the Department of Welfare, Community Development Agency, Youth Board, and the Manpower and Career Development Agency.

2. The Housing and Development Administration, which includes the Housing and Redevelopment Board Department of Buildings and the Rent and Rehabilitation Administration.

3. The Recreation and Cultural Affairs Administration, which includes the Department of Parks, the Office of Cultural Affairs, Libraries, and Museums.

4. The Health Services Administration, which includes the Department of Health, Community Mental Health Board, and the Department of Hospitals.

This Health Services Administration has committed itself to the establishment of ambulatory health services for the Multiservice Center, which is to include all of those medical and mental health services that can appropriately and economically be provided outside of a hospital proper. The Lincoln Hospital Mental Health Services, in collaboration with the Health Services Administration (on what we might describe as the strategic level) and the Community Mental Health Board (on a more frequent tactical level) will establish neighborhood-based components of a mental health center within this context. These Neighborhood Mental Health Units, as they are designated, will in essence offer the greater part of those services previously provided during the demonstration period, either in the Neighborhood Service Center or within the Multipurpose Clinical Facility. The new Neighborhood Mental Health Units will include outpatient services, partial hospitalization for adults, adolescents, and children, rehabilitation services, precare and aftercare services, diagnostic, consultation, and education services. These various services will be closely linked with additional services primarily based in the general hospital, even though such services will also be represented to a limited extent in the neighborhood-based unit. These include administrative functions, research and evaluation, training, certain emergency services, and consultation programs with medical and surgical departments. Adult inpatient services will be located at the nearby Bronx State Hospital, where wards have been established specifically designated for psychotic patients from the Multiservice Center area.

Although the above outline may convey some notion of the services to be established in connection with the Neighborhood Mental Health Unit, and almost all of these services have already been in operation previously, their introduction into the Multiservice Center will produce alterations which can only be partially anticipated from the prior experimental and demonstration programs. The Multiservice Center itself will contribute a unique emphasis and direction that grows out of such characteristic features as integration and coordination of various service components, decentralization and relative autonomy of service operation, community participation in the planning and development of services, and training and utilization of local manpower for the actual operation of the Multiservice Center.

Integration and Coordination of Service Components

Like most other mental health services, the initial location of the Lincoln program was dictated primarily by considerations of expediency. The general hospital was the primary base because of the major role of the New York City Department of Hospitals in establishing the program. This location, while isolated somewhat from the community, had the advantage of giving us access to medical services and to our colleagues in other medical departments. Within this setting, some of our consultative community programs were established in conjunction with such agencies as schools, day care, and community centers. The establishment of the Neighborhood Service Center-Medical Health Aide program helped meet some of the special needs of the particular agency, neighborhood, or population, but it also tended to produce units separate from each other and from the clinical center of the mental health facility. Thus, there is a tendency to produce the very fragmentation a comprehensive community mental health program is designed to minimize. It is anticipated that the incorporation of the proposed Lincoln Hospital Neighborhood Mental Health Units into the Model Cities Multiservice Center will counter this trend.

Combination of a common administrative structure for various units of the Multiservice Center, as well as actual geographic proximity, should allow for greater comprehensiveness of the mental health program while facilitating integration with the pertinent health and human services, such as other medical departments, welfare, housing, manpower, and youth, etc. Although this multiplicity of services in itself poses a substantial problem in organization, the relatively small size of the area to be served should allow for a more manageable unit than prevails in the larger, more centralized structures.

Decentralization and Autonomy

Neighborhood-based services lend themselves to decentralization and encourage the development of more autonomous units capable of being more responsive to the needs of the local community. The relatively small size of such units can be utilized to reduce the bureaucratic pressures toward depersonalization of services and thereby allow for greater flexibility and informality. It is evident that the size of the unit will not in itself assure the attainment of any of these objectives, but merely is one of the important conditions that can assist in bringing about a number of interrelated goals.

Among these various goals for both the community as a whole as well as its constituents, individuals, families, groups, and organizations, the movement toward autonomy is central. In a previous publication (Peck, 1963) it was noted that autonomy occupies a very central role among the six criteria of positive mental health cited by Jahoda (1958).[4] She summarizes the various defining concepts of autonomy by characterizing it as "a relation between individual and environment with regard to decision making." Jahoda quotes Riesman's (1950) definition of autonomous persons as those "capable of conforming to the behavior norms of their society but who remain free to choose whether to conform or not." Autonomy defined in these terms may be utilized as a major criterion of both an individual's competence or mental health, as well as an indicator of the level of development of the families, groups, and organizations that comprise a community. Decentralization represents the capacity to transfer decision-making from a centrally vested authority to the peripheral subunits of an organization. Just as the small size of the Neighborhood Mental Health Unit only facilitates but does not assure decentralization, so an organization capable of decentralization only encourages but does not in itself bring about autonomous functioning either in groups or individuals. However, the approaches discussed under the sections below on Community Participation and on Training represent several of the major avenues for the attainment of autonomy, as well as other associated mental health objectives.

Community Participation in Planning and Development

The service needs of a community like the South Bronx are almost infinite. Yet at any given moment there are only limited resources, funds, and facilities available. The priorities should bear some relationship to the wishes of those most vitally concerned, the residents of the community. In a neighborhood-based unit, it is more feasible for the community in conjunction with professional personnel to set such priorities. The community group planning the Multiservice Center in the South Bronx is a subcommittee of the Hunts Point Community Corporation. The Community Corporation is the local agency which, in collaboration with the New York City Community Development Administration, processes the Office of Economic Opportunity funded programs for the neighborhood. The leadership of the Community Corporation is primarily composed of citizens of the community who were elected to the office by the area's residents. It is anticipated that as the Multiservice Center is developed, the present committee structure will be replaced by a permanent governing body. If the present guidelines are followed, professional and agency interests will be represented, but the determination of policy will be retained by the residents of the community. For the present, the Multiservice Center Subcommittee on Health and Mental Health Services has drawn on professional staff from

---

[4]The six criteria that Jahoda derives from an extensive review of the literature are: (1) attitudes toward the self; (2) growth, development, and self-actualization; (3) integration; (4) autonomy; (5) perception of reality; and (6) environmental mastery.

agencies such as the Lincoln Hospital Mental Health Services for advice. We have been asked to submit proposals and are utilized as resources and advisory personnel to those residents of the community who constitute the primary sponsoring body of the Multiservice Center. A program that is established under such auspices is more likely to elicit community support and ultimately lead to the establishment of high quality services. The maintenance of such quality is of primary concern to the potential recipients of services, and it is their participation in the program that is the best assurance of continued efforts at improvements.

Changes in the mental health agency's role growing out of its participation in the Model Cities program go beyond improvements in the quality and range of direct services to the population of the area. The extent to which such improvements can significantly alter the overwhelming tide of pathology in the community is limited by the availability of resources. Indeed improvement in resources and facilities seems to be in a desperate race against the progressive deterioration of these same facilities. It has been our position that unless improvement in services is accompanied by changes in the community's institutional structure, the outcome of this race will remain very much in doubt. Major changes must be instituted both within the formal agencies of the community and in such aspects of its informal structure as the family and those community groups that are the essential context of the day-to-day life of the residents. The strategy that has thus far been described is viewed as a base from which such changes can be mounted. Like most struggles, however, its effectiveness will be largely determined by the numbers and kinds of people who can be mobilized to carry it out.

Training and Utilization of Local Manpower

Shortages of personnel impair the effectiveness of various essential services in many communities. It is generally recognized that the nation as a whole is inadequately supplied with such professionals as doctors, nurses, social workers, and teachers, as well as the many kinds of technicians and paraprofessional personnel who work in association with them. Programs located in the lower socioeconomic areas are often those most seriously handicapped by personnel shortages and experience the greatest difficulty in attracting qualified staff. These manpower shortages in the urban ghettoes are truly paradoxical in view of the high unemployment rates and the many people who work below their capacity in the very areas that do not have sufficient personnel to man their essential services.

The kind of solutions to the manpower problem represented in the establishment of the Mental Health Aide program at Lincoln is only a beginning. This approach need not be confined to the mental health agency, nor should recruitment for a variety of health and human services be limited to entry level jobs. It is not economical to mount separate recruitment and training components for each category of service. What is called for is a careers and training program covering a broad range of health and human services, linked to an extended system of job, progression and supported by facilities for formal educational advancement and certification. Such an arrangement is clearly an essential concomitant to the effective operation of the kind of Multiservice Center envisioned for the Model Cities program. Although the implementation of such a program will almost inevitably have to tap governmental and other resources outside of the neighborhood to be served by the Multiservice Center, it is crucial to the effectiveness of the enterprise that the local community be fully involved in each step from the initial planning to the final implementation of the program. This approach has been incorporated into a Health Careers Program currently being planned under the auspices of the Lincoln Hospital-Albert Einstein College of Medicine[5] (Peck, Levin, & Roman, 1967). It is anticipated that this program will utilize the facilities of the Hunts Point Multiservice Center as a major laboratory for the program once it is in operation. Plans call for participation by the local community from its very inception. The community is to have representation in establishing policies and priorities, participate in the selection of candidates for training, and have a voice in the planning of the training program. It is anticipated that this type of community participation will reinforce the continuing responsibility of trainees to the community they are to serve and contribute to the maintenance of high quality services.

The recruitment of trainees from the community who will have a common training experience will also assist in the integration of the various service units for which they are trained. Similarly, the participation of professional training personnel from the different agencies should help consolidate the relationships between the various service units. The establishment of joint training programs at all levels where it is feasible and desirable will, it is hoped, facilitate future collaboration when such trainees work as staff members with their different agencies. It is axiomatic that "people who learn together work together," providing, of course, that the learning experience is a positive one.

The introduction of people from the community into the establishment agencies is not only designed to improve the quality of services, it is also conducive to the development of community competence and autonomy. As people from the community become more closely associated with the actual operation of the various agencies, the community will become more aware and knowledgeable about issues directly affecting its own health and mental health. Finally, increased access to the pertinent information and the introduction of community people into the policy and decision-making process of the agencies will raise the

[5]Planning for the Lincoln Hospital, Albert Einstein College of Medicine Health Careers Program is currently supported by a grant from the Commonwealth Foundation for a three-year period beginning in September, 1967.

community's ability to master and control significant aspects of its environment. This process represents one of the major ways through which the overall mental health status of the community may be enhanced. However, definitive knowledge regarding the extent to which this process actually occurs and the conditions necessary to its operation must be the subject of a broad and continuing program of research and evaluation.

Research and Evaluation

About one year after the launching of the Neighborhood Service Center-Mental Health Aide Program in 1965, a grant from the National Institute of Mental Health enabled the Lincoln Hospital Mental Health Services to establish a formal research unit. In the most general sense, the purpose of this research unit was to contribute to the development of effective community mental health centers. A series of studies and projects were conceptualized and implemented to form an integrated program of research designed to accomplish the following specific purposes:

a. to develop meaningful systems of information as one basis for planning and implementing community mental health center programs;

b. to develop methods for documenting and evaluating the performance of the various components of community mental health centers, particularly as related to explicitly stated goals;

c. to develop procedures for the selection, assessment, and evaluation of mental health personnel;

d. to gain an understanding of the community—its social organizations, communication networks, needs, and preferences—in relationship to the goals and services of a community mental health center.

A record-keeping system was first developed to provide a comprehensive description of clients of the Neighborhood Service Centers. Included is a description of each client in terms of family composition, demographic variables, referral source, services rendered, and location in a specific social area of the catchment area. This system was conceptualized as a prototype and is currently being generalized to other components of Lincoln Hospital Mental Health Services as it evolves into a community mental health center. It is partially automated and has ambitions to produce, in addition to meaningful summary statistics, a protocol of useful information when stimulated by an electronic message. Since this record-keeping system was developed as a prototype, it would be readily adaptable to use by the other components of the Multiservice Center. Such coordination in recording would constitute an important contribution to the consolidation and integration of services.

It is an explicit assumption that clinical services take on an added dimension of meaning if the clinician understands the environment in which clients participate as residents and citizens. One of our projects is to identify those variables that meaningfully describe a set of homogenous social areas composing the catchment area. These variables describe each social area in terms of dwelling, population and occupation characteristics (conceptualized as predictor variables), and a set of outcome variables assumed to be theoretically linked to environmental conditions. The outcome variables are exemplified by hospitalization for mental illness, the use of medical facilities, the production of premature children, and the frequency of arrests. In addition to their obvious value for planning, the magnitude of relationships among these predictor and outcome variables (and they are very high) indicate the extent to which environmental conditions and these outcome variables are related. We believe this pattern of relationships has implications for the type and extent of intervention necessary for change. The broad range and type of information produced by such studies would have special relevance both in planning for a neighborhood mental health unit that is to be a component of a Multiservice Center and for the Multiservice Center itself.

A combination of the information of our record systems and the social areas study provides an understanding of the selective use of health and mental health facilities. The use of services may be easily related to both the personal characteristics of clients and the environments in which they live.

A series of survey studies of selected populations of citizens in the catchment area provides yet another level of information. The subject matter of our surveys has ranged from population characteristics to community needs, to the use and evaluation of the Neighborhood Service Centers. The results of these studies exemplify the usefulness of this procedure for answering questions of administrators, program directors, and researchers which, in many cases, grow out of the output of record systems and the social areas studies.

Our anthropological studies, focused on social organizations and communication networks, provide another view of the residents of the catchment area. In particular, the relationships among mental health relevant concepts, such as social participation, interpersonal competence and coping behavior, and the kind and degree of involvement in the social organizations of the area, are of vital interest both to mental health programs and to the Multiservice Center as a whole. Social organizations are potential members of a network that, ideally, serves the needs of the community and actualizes the many potentials of its residents.

An important need of a mental health network is personnel with a genuine interest in the welfare of the people in the catchment area. To be of value this interest must be combined with the ability and desire to become effective community mental health personnel. To this end we are developing a set of procedures for the selection, assessment, and evaluation of mental health personnel. These procedures attempt to provide a reasonable basis for tapping the enormous potential of catchment areas for those citizens most likely to become effective mental health workers. Although standards would be different, we believe that some of the same procedures could be developed for the selection and training of other Multiservice Center staff drawn from the community. The opportunity for establishing joint programs of recruitment, selection, and training by the various components of the Multiservice Center opens the way to procedures for introducing into the system those members of the community best suited to perform the various functions of the Center.

A program of research and evaluation along the lines briefly summarized above is clearly an essential element of a neighborhood mental health unit of the type we have described. It is almost indispensable to a mental health program within a Multiservice Center if both are to have some systematic basis for modifying their combined operations in response to community need.[6]

Comprehensive community mental health centers and the Model Cities Multiservice Centers are both in the various stages of planning and early implementation across the nation. There would appear to be common tasks, problems, and strategies confronting both types of organizations sufficient to warrant serious collaborative planning.

The Lincoln Hospital Mental Health Services have, over the past several years, been engaged in research, demonstration, and training projects that seem pertinent to such joint efforts. In this connection, we have reviewed some of our experiences, concepts, and approaches. On the basis of our progress to date, we feel justified in encouraging our psychiatric colleagues working in urban mental health programs to seriously consider participation with Multiservice Centers or comparable agencies. Similarly, we trust that this report will provide some guide to nonpsychiatrists engaged in the developing of Model Cities and Multiservice Centers programs when they call upon their local mental health centers for assistance. Despite the newness of the programs presently being developed, the recognition that psychiatrists and mental health services are intimately related to the total range of health and human needs is hardly a recent discovery. Collaboration between the Model Cities Multiservice Center and the comprehensive community mental health center seems, however, to be an excellent way of effectively implementing what we have long known.

---

[6]More detailed material on research and evaluation is available in the Lincoln Hospital Mental Health Services Research Progress Reports for 1966 and 1967 and in the paper by Struening and Peck (1968).

References

Jahoda, M. *Current concepts of positive mental health.* New York: Basic Books, 1958.

Logue Report. New York: Institute of Public Administration, 1966.

Peck, H. Some relationships between group process and mental health phenomena in theory and practice. *International Journal of Group Psychotherapy,* 1963, *13,* 269–289.

Peck, H., & Kaplan, S. Crisis theory and therapeutic change in small groups: some implementations for community mental health programs. *Psychotherapy,* 1966, *16,* 135–149.

Peck, H., Kaplan, S., & Roman, M. Prevention, treatment, and social action: A strategy of intervention in a disadvantaged urban area. *American Journal of Orthopsychiatry,* 1966, *36,* 57–69.

Peck, H., Levin, T., & Roman, M. The health careers institute: A mental health strategy for an urban community. American Journal of Psychiatry, in press.

Riesman, D., Glazer, N., & Kenney, R. *The lonely crowd.* New Haven: Yale University Press, 1950.

Struening, E., & Peck, H. The role of research in goal determination and program evaluation: A case history from an urban mental health center. In R. H. Williams & L. D. Ozarin (Eds.), *Community mental health: An international perspective. Part II: Programs and Research Issues.* San Francisco: Jossey-Bass, 1968. Pp. 167–201.

Part III
Programs with a
Problem-Solving Orientation

New programs are often generated as a response to specific problems within the community. Although the program may take many forms, its success ultimately depends upon whether or not it has successfully solved the problem that generated the program. One such problem is delinquency. Urban, suburban, and rural areas have all been concerned about the rise in antisocial behavior. The causes and forms of this behavior differ, so that the approaches for dealing with the problem must also differ.

In this section, two programs dealing with the problem of delinquency in divergent settings are presented. Within the inner city, delinquency is strongly related to the general social disorganization. The mental health worker, therefore, finds it imperative to get involved in aspects other than just the motivational dynamics of the individual. In suburbia, on the other hand, where many opportunities are available, antisocial behavior is more closely tied to the individual's psychodynamics. But even there certain social forces may operate to alienate youth. Therefore, it becomes necessary to work with groups in the community to reestablish those links that make constructive social development possible.

Chapter 8
Priorities in Social Services
for the Slum Neighborhood

Harold H. Weissman

A mental health program may start with a very specific goal, such as the reduction of certain disruptive or symptomatic behaviors. However, as this develops, many unforeseen problems may arise, requiring new involvement on the part of mental health personnel, often in areas they have customarily avoided. The history of the Mobilization for Youth (MFY) program in New York is a case in point. Although the program was originally set up as a demonstration project aimed at increasing the opportunity structure in order to reduce delinquency, it was found that major changes in the whole social structure of the community became necessary. In order to deal with and alter the social structure, many new roles have evolved for mental health professionals and nonprofessionals. One such role is that of the facilitator or expeditor,[1] often an indigenous worker who serves to help the individual find his way through the existing social agency structure so that he can receive the services that he requires in an efficient way (this role is an elaboration of that of the ombudsman in Sweden). Dr. Weissman, in the following chapter, suggests that the mental health worker may at times need to go beyond acting as facilitator and become still more active and involved in bringing about social action. He suggests that the mental health professional may indeed have to take on the role of an advocate, a role that has many political implications. In this role he is required to select areas of intervention that he considers critical in effecting change. Because of the multitude of unmet needs, it is impossible for mental health personnel to meet all the needs expressed by the community. It is his feeling, therefore, that it becomes obligatory for the mental health professional to use his knowledge of the needs of the community in order to mobilize the community into constructive action.

[1]The role of the facilitator-expeditor was conceptualized by Reiff, R. and Riessman, F., in "The Indigenous Non-professional: A Strategy of Change in Community Action and Community Mental Health Program," published by Behavioral Publications, Inc., New York City, and forms part of the program described by Peck and Kaplan in their chapter in this volume.

Chapter 8

Priorities in Social Services
for the Slum Neighborhood

Harold H. Weissman

Social work has a long history of neighborhood work. After briefly tracing this history, this chapter attempts to delineate a set of priorities for services in the slums through examination of a case history of how priorities were set in a relatively new social welfare institution—the neighborhood service center.

The charity organization societies of the 19th century divided cities into administrative districts, which often coincided with existing neighborhood designations, so that the distribution of charity could be handled efficiently and smoothly. These societies operated in the belief that agency service would be improved if people who were aware of local conditions were also administratively responsible. They conceived of the neighborhood primarily as an administrative area.

Workers in settlement houses enlarged upon this view. The neighborhoods in which they worked were viewed as the spawning grounds of social problems. Poor sanitation, gambling, vice, inadequate recreational facilities, overcrowding, and a host of other social ills were felt to be the causes of people's problems. For each neighborhood there were the same generalized goals—a good, clean, healthy, well-serviced environment. Change the environment, and you change the person. Both the charity organization societies and the settlement houses, in a sense, defined the neighborhood as the area in which they offered service.

In 1923 Ernest Burgess, speaking to the National Conference of Social Work, added another dimension to the thinking of social workers about neighborhoods. Where previously neighborhoods were seen as areas in need of improvement, Burgess stressed their existing positive aspects. ". . . The pivotal consideration for placing social work on a local basis inheres in the very fact that city life has lost its local character. It is this change that accounts for the disorder, disorganization, and confusion of our most rapidly growing cities" (Burgess, 1926, p. 505). He pointed to the loss of security and loneliness of city dwellers when face-to-face primary relationships disappear. His ideas found a receptive audience. The idea of the lonely, atomized city dweller has been a favorite among social workers.

In the same vein, but with slightly different emphasis, Robert Wood, in his influential work, *The Neighborhood in Nation Building,* pointed out the necessity of promoting citizen interest in preserving socially decent neighborhoods. If citizens did not take an active interest in the affairs of their neighborhood, how could they gain the experience and knowledge to promote good government in their city and country. In addition, if citizens took an interest in their neighborhoods, not only would democracy be strengthened but also the city dweller would be able to develop a sense of belonging through civic participation that would go a long way towards dissipating the inherent loneliness of city life.

Out of such neighborhood traditions of service, Mobilization for Youth began operations in the summer of 1962. Its theoretical and operational base was formulated by sociologists Richard Cloward and Lloyd Ohlin in *A Proposal for the Prevention and Control of Delinquency by Expanding Opportunities.* For them the slum neighborhood did not offer the social, economic, or psychological resources or opportunities to make conformity to society's values possible. Thus, Mobilization for Youth was begun in 1962 as the first comprehensive, demonstration, and research project funded through Federal, city, and private foundation sources, geared to eradicating the evils of poverty, delinquency, and social disorganization in the urban slum. The agency's target area included approximately 107,000 people living in an elongated L-shaped sliver of New York's Lower East Side. This famous ghetto was quickly changing from a Jewish to a Puerto Rican homeland.

In 1962, and increasing steadily with each year, the area was 30% Puerto Rican and 10% Negro. (By 1967 the white population was clearly in the minority.) Forty percent of the housing in the area was substandard, mostly old law tenements. The delinquency rate was nearly the highest in the city, and drug addiction was rampant. Over 40% of the population received some sort of governmental financial assistance. Unemployment and underemployment were double the city's average. Among Negroes and Puerto Ricans over 30% of all households were headed by a female.

The project's planners, made up of social scientists from Columbia University, social workers in the existing Lower East Side settlements, and representatives of city government and prestigious social welfare interest groups, assumed that existing community resources and opportunities were either unavailable or insufficiently accessible to lower-income people. The agency's program proposals were divided into five main areas: work training, education, community development, legal assistance, and case service to individuals and families. The overriding targets of the demonstration projects in these areas were institutional change, programmatic innovation, development of practice techniques, and assessment of the impact of all the programs on the neighborhood.

The Neighborhood Service Centers (NSC), a major programmatic innovation of the project, were to be the doors through which the low-income client could approach the new services and opportunities housed at Mobilization. In order to understand how the agency set its priorities as well as to arrive at some of the bases upon which priorities for neighborhood services might be set, a brief description of the program history of these service centers follows.

Neighborhood Service Centers

These "helping stations," as they were initially described, were to be staffed by caseworkers adept at mediating differences, particularly between low-income people and public agencies, but also adept at counseling and making knowledgeable referrals to a wide range of social services in the interest of their clients. The Centers were to be accessible, located in storefronts in the heart of the neighborhoods. Staff were to be trained in a cheerful and friendly nonbureaucratic approach to clients. Appointments would not be required, nor would long forms and records be a requisite for service. The major goal cited by the Proposal was the reduction of self-defeating attitudes on the part of clients, including such phenomena as defeatism, powerlessness, a general lack of interest, hopelessness, and pessimism.

Social workers professionally prepared to give long-term counseling were hired, as well as other personnel skilled in giving immediate concrete service, e.g., homemakers, child care assistants, etc. The idea was that the Neighborhood Service Center would supply whatever material and psychological supports were necessary to move the client to a more stable level of functioning—and on to the appropriate opportunity.

Operationalizing the ideas spelled out in the Proposal for the Service Centers was the task of the professional staff. Prior to opening the first Center, several months were spent discussing procedures, finding suitable storefront locations, hiring additional staff, and arguing over what was really meant by the "new casework" that was to be developed at the Centers.

While the Proposal speaks about the need for a neighborhood advisory committee for the Centers, almost three years passed before the clients were involved in the actual operation of the Centers, and then in a way not anticipated in the Proposal. Policy at the Centers, prior to their opening, was really dictated by the experimental and demonstration needs of the total project and was thus staff controlled. These concerns were clearly put in the Proposal:

> . . . we believe that much is yet to be learned about the way in which changes in human behavior can be forcefully induced by deliberately reordering the social environment of the individual. What we wish to stress is the reconstruction of the individual's social conditions through a casework process so that he then experiences new pressures which exert a direct influence on him for change in a preconceived direction . . . The question we must answer is: What types of person can be expected to be influenced in what ways by what types of program? (Mobilization for Youth, 1961, p. 357)

When the first Neighborhood Service Center opened, the plan was to offer differential service based on the need of the client. At the onset of the program cases were classified in two ways. Social planning cases were those that required ongoing counseling with the client over a long period of time, e.g., the typical multiproblem family. Social broker cases were those where only immediate help with requests for concrete services was required, e.g., a tenant threatened with eviction. Very soon after the Centers began operation the pressure for providing service, particularly in the social broker areas with the limited staff available, became paramount. Ultimately, after only a few months of actual operation staff were restricted to handling only 10% social planning cases. It became unmistakably clear that clients wanted help with various so-called service institutions—welfare, schools, hospitals, clinics. A decision was made to serve only clients with problems that centered around the use of public and private service agencies; other problems would be referred and not accepted for service.

A description by Elman of the life situation of the clients of the Neighborhood Service Centers gives a clear indication of the reasons for the policy shift from a focus on individual change to a focus on how agencies function for individuals and agency change.

"In recent years numerous Puerto Rican families have become trapped in deteriorating tenements. Estimates range as high as 20% for the number of Puerto Rican families on public assistance, most of them in the ADC category. Living in what was virtually a welfare ghetto, remote from all the service institutions on the Lower East Side, many of these large fatherless families existed between welfare checks through expensive credit arrangements with neighborhood grocers.

As early as the third of each month the dispossess notices began to appear in the hallway mailboxes and under the rodent-proofed doorways of Stanton Street. These were a regular service of the landlords, anxious under the Rent Control Laws of the City of New York to increase rent by creating a turnover among apartment holders whom they would try to force to vacate. To avoid default judgment, tenants would have to appear in the landlord-tenant's court on Center Street many blocks away. If it was a case of Welfare withholding rent against the correction of building violations, the tenant would have to contend with the court, with his investigator, as well as with his landlord. Other days' mail might bring dunning notifications from Household Finance or from Consolidated Edison that gas and electricity were being cut off, summonses to appear in civil court to explain why the purchaser was reluctant to pay nearly three times the original price in credit and service charges on a sewing machine of dubious mechanical function. Although it was perfectly true that Stanton Street residents were not particularly litigious, they were confronted throughout their daily lives by individuals and institutions which are.

The principal welfare center for residents of Stanton Street is located in what was once a red brick school house across the street from a police station. You enter the Lower Manhattan Center past an armed guard; almost immediately you are confronted by a small desk where you are given your first brief interview. This initial orientation, or "softening up" interview as one worker described it, serves the specific purpose of making certain that the person has come to the right office for the right kind of service. But it seems to fit into the general purpose of all interviewing procedures at DW which is to cast immediate suspicion on the applicant to make him come forth

[1]This quote was taken from a Mobilization for Youth untitled working paper on Neighborhood Service Centers by Richard Elman, pp. 4–6. The same description can be found in expanded form in the Cloward and Elman references cited in the text.

with proof that he does not have income. Not knowing what may lie ahead of him, applicants will often rattle off their life details of adversity at this desk, only to be peremptorily informed to 'save it for the investigator' (Cloward & Elman, 1967, pp. 253-256)."

By January of 1964 the program of the Neighborhood Service Centers had solidified. The distinction between social broker and social planning cases in effect did not exist. Clients continually returned with problems with welfare, schools, courts, etc., yet there really was no time for long-term counseling as was envisioned in the social planning cases. A report in 1964 notes that limiting service to the provision of concrete environmental services relative to helping people make better use of community resources did not limit the number of cases at the four Centers. At that time the average caseload per worker was 32, and clients might be seen anywhere from one to six times a week. Seventy-four percent of the cases were Puerto Rican, 20% Negro, and 6% white. Seventy-five percent of these cases were known to the Department of Welfare, and 70% of the families were living in tenements. In light of these statistics there was no question that the NSC's had reached and continued to reach and serve the low-income population of the MFY area.

By mid-1964 staff were defining their role as advocates. Advocacy has been defined as the willingness to intervene with a government agency on behalf of a low-income person.

"It does not mean helping the poor man to help himself or enabling him to better manage his transactions with the governmental department. It means filling in the power deficit on his side of the transaction by providing him with an advocate who has specialized knowledge of the rules and regulations of the system (this includes its informal and thus unstated innerworkings, which, though obscure from general view, may nevertheless prove of major significance in understanding how decisions get made and how they can get changed). But most of all, advocacy means a readiness to become an adversary, to pit oneself against the system with whatever means at hand, whether skills in persuasion, manipulation, or straight forward pressure."[2]

Welfare problems were central to the NSC experience over the years. There had, however, been considerable activity in other areas. Staff was active in the field of education. They kept in constant touch with teachers and helped to interpret to them those aspects of family life that made the educational process difficult for the young child. Matters such as illness, family attitudes toward education, language problems, housing conditions, and cultural differences were discussed and interpreted to the teachers. In the case of the prejudiced teacher or the teacher who engaged in physical violence, social workers came forward as advocates, using their knowledge and power in behalf of the alienated parent and child. Social workers also became advocates in relation to various failings in the educational system, most particularly the kangaroo court procedures that characterized some of the suspension hearings.

In the health area, advocacy became necessary for a number of reasons. Large

[2]This quote was taken from the above-mentioned source by Elman, p. 41.

municipal hospitals, and particularly their emergency rooms, can be quite confusing. Clients may have to deal with long waiting lines, a number of separate appointments, which people whose English is limited may find especially hard to understand, or a series of different doctors on separate visits for the same illness. Nonmedical personnel at a hospital may treat a patient rudely, a welfare recipient may go through a number of weeks spending money for carfare without receiving reimbursement, or the patient may even come to feel that he is a human guinea pig in the hands of a medical student, if the medical school is interested in that patient's particular illness.

In their attempts to help clients through this maze, workers were hindered by as much as three months' delay in the receipt of information from medical records, or social service departments in the hospitals so overburdened they could do little but process forms. Nevertheless, staff actively and aggressively intervened with hospitals to achieve a number of results. When a mother was diagnosed as tubercular, children were x-rayed without the usual delay; hasty judgments about retardation have been reevaluated, avoiding unnecessary institutional commitment; and clients were saved from being hastily and incorrectly admitted to mental wards.

The advocacy stance of the Centers dictated another set of priorities. To make medical care possible, ancillary services had to be provided, such as the provision of escorts who help get a person to a clinic and also interpret the medical situation and hospital structure. Another important service has been the provision of money for carfare. Hundreds of dollars annually have been dispensed to families with young children for use as carfare. The Centers decided early that the risk could not be taken of a client's refusing to take young children to the clinic or make regular visits to a prenatal clinic because MFY and the Welfare Department were wrangling over where the responsibility for carfare rested. The Centers also granted or loaned funds for such items as eyeglasses, summer camp physical examinations, emergency dental care, and the like when it became apparent that unreasonable delays would injure the health of a young child, for instance, or the stability of a family.

A child care service was instituted to provide short-term babysitting service for young mothers, a service that went far towards relieving the tensions and strains of everyday living. This service was basically custodial, but it was also used to uncover a number of unmet needs. Cases were found of children under the age of three who were legally blind, or almost deaf, or retarded, and whose parents were not aware of the situation. In addition, by placing well children in a care station during a clinic visit, mothers were able to give more attention to the sick children and avoid having to deal with disciplinary problems in the impersonal atmosphere of a clinic waiting room.

By mid-1965, as the months passed, it became clear that the advocacy stance of the workers was successful in achieving concrete gains for the vast majority of clients, but in and of itself was not particularly useful for bringing about broad changes in the policy of the Department of Welfare. At this point the decision was made to organize groups of clients to seek changes in Department of Welfare procedures and policies through organized community action. The rationale for this partial shift in emphasis in the NSC's from worker advocacy to client advocacy was stated as follows:

> "The task of the community developer is to organize clients as a group for purposes of taking social action against common problems. The new program has two purposes. First, we are convinced that such action is necessary if bureaucratic service institutions are to be made more responsive to people's needs. The second purpose is to experiment with the implementation of the hypothesis that participation in such activities is therapeutic to the client."[1]

Ultimately, six welfare groups were organized. Not only did they literally recover hundreds of thousands of dollars legally due their members, but they were also successful in gaining the commitment of large numbers of clients for minimum standards and winter clothing campaigns, fair hearing appeals, and a variety of training programs. Most heartening was the fact that many of the leaders of the groups, as well as ordinary members, ultimately were able to make use of training programs set up through Office of Economic Opportunity funds and get off the welfare rolls.

Implications for Planning

The Neighborhood Service Centers tapped a vast reservoir of unmet needs of the poor on the Lower East Side. The Centers served over 8,000 families and 35,000 different people in five years of operation. The amount of help given is overwhelming, weighed against the fact that no help would have been available without the Center's services. A number of implications can be drawn for setting service priorities.

Jane Addams is reported to have said to one of her students, "Young man, I do not believe in geographical salvation" (quoted by Berry, 1962, p. 190). She did not mean that the neighborhood was an inappropriate location for social services; rather she understood that neighborhoods should not be viewed as neat, clearly demarcated, nonoverlapping sections of the city. Planning from this point of view could only lead to devising tidy standards of service based on abstract ideals for good neighborhoods—so many parks per 10,000 population, so many caseworkers, etc. Rather, planning must be done on the basis of what exists and from the MFY experience in slum neighborhoods, diversity of people and conflict among their needs is the paramount and significant factor.

The Neighborhood Service Centers began with the idea that they were going to meet the needs of the clients as the clients defined them. The Centers would

[1]This quote and the preceeding five paragraphs are adapted from Barr, 1965, pp. 19–24.

avoid the professional trap of defining the needs of clients in terms of the professionals' expertise, whether casework, psychiatry, vocational counseling, etc. Initially what was insufficiently realized was that there were too many needs and too few resources to meet them. Ultimately in situations of limited resources, a decision must be taken as to which needs must be met. To say that the people must decide is to partially beg the question, for some at one time will want help with welfare, others with school problems, then medical problems, and the like. There are so many urgent unmet needs, one compounding the other, that an administrator can only be perplexed as to what to do first.

Consider the case of Tomasa Buenaventura:

> Tomasa Buenaventura is a slender, once-beautiful woman in her fifties who wears her black hair in a ponytail that sways gently, girlishly when she speaks to you. There is no end to the variety of her expression, her grace, and gesture. But Tomasa Buenaventura's life is not a success story. She is a chronic alcoholic, now diagnosed an alcoholic-psychotic. Her husband of 20 years deserted her a few years ago. She speaks no English, has no income, and is entirely supported by the New York State Department of Welfare. The youngest of her eight children, Ricky, is 14 and lives with his mother in a three-room apartment on Third Street near Avenue C. Ricky is in the sixth grade at P.S. 64, on Ninth Street near Avenue B. More than anything else, he is fond of his pigeons, which he keeps on the roof. Until recently he had never seen Ninth Street near Fifth Avenue, only fourteen blocks from his home. He equates age with shrinking and is sure that his dog, Senor Kikko, is smaller at four years than he was at three. He speaks very little of his family.
>
> One brother, Carlos, just older than Ricky, has been in Bellevue Hospital TB Ward for the past six months. The next oldest, Rafael, has just returned from State Training School; though he was supposed to stay with an older sister, his whereabouts are presently unknown. The rest of Mrs. Buenaventura's children are married, and most have children of their own. They see their father occasionally, more often accidentally when they bump into him on the street. Formerly an alcoholic himself, Mr. Buenaventura has stopped drinking and for the past two years has held a steady job as an attendant at Bellevue Hospital. He now lives with another woman, somewhere in the same neighborhood.

What does she need? Obviously many things—a typical "multiproblem family." Yet in planning services is it sufficient to provide workers whose function is to counsel with multiproblem families? Such a unit was set up in another MFY program. Involvement with the families of its target population resulted in a substantial increase in the number of persons, all with problems that required consideration and time, for whom the unit became virtually responsible. Of the first 28 cases the unit received in 1963, the families consisted of a total of 47 adults and 122 children, which meant 169 human beings to be serviced, not just the 28 assigned to the project. Forty-three percent of those families were receiving public assistance and required information to help with food, housing, health problems, and sometimes direct financial assistance when emergencies arose. In addition, the average family was involved with at least four social agencies, typically public assistance, health services, housing assistance, and various community center services. A report noted that when plans for optimal treatment were made it was found that an average of five additional services would have to be provided. (One family had been known to 16 agencies in the area.) Even with the small caseload each worker carried, many were involved in evening and weekend work.

In planning services, the vantage point one takes is crucial. Looked at simply from the point of view of what is best done for Mrs. Buenaventura, setting up a multiproblem counseling unit makes sense. From the point of view of thousands of Mrs. Buenaventuras on the Lower East Side or in any slum neighborhood, such an approach is not feasible given the lack of integration current and the ineffectiveness of services. While many are struggling with long-range plans for making effective the tangled webs of fragmented and inadequate services for the poor (Beck, 1967; Harris, 1967), short-range policy must be set to deal with the present situation of inadequate resources and services. This inevitably means that some needs will not be met.

The Mobilization experience points to certain priorities. The overwhelming demand for help with welfare problems and the enthusiastic response to job training programs are indicative of one set of program priorities for the poor. The poor develop ways of coping that are often called self-defeating but that they see as necessary for their survival—attitudes and values that lend themselves to concepts of "live for today and don't worry about tomorrow," problems in organizing time, planning ahead, delaying gratification, etc. It is clear that these self-defeating attitudes cannot be overcome unless the poor see some possibility of attaining economic security. Only when this is achieved, when life is no longer living from one survival crisis to another, will they really be able to contemplate more sophisticated problems.

Programmatically this means that attention in slums must be given to problems related to employment, public welfare, job training, consumer affairs, and the like. This means when the choice is between a mental hygiene unit and a day-care service, the priority is day care. If a choice must be made between better health services or job-training services, the answer is jobs. The hard truth is that those who plan are seldom willing to accept such a priority choice, preferring to create a public image of an all-encompassing service.

In setting priorities, it cannot be contended that needs ignored do not exist. For example, there is little doubt that the poor need psychological counseling more than the rich. Yet to attempt such counseling without being able to deal with the concrete life problems faced by the poor is to attempt social sorcery. Long ago Freud noted that "we shall probably discover that the poor are even less ready to part with their neuroses than the rich because the life that awaits them when they recover has no attraction" (quoted by Coles, 1964, p. 11).

A second short-run priority that can be drawn from the MFY experience is the vital need of the poor for advocates. They simply are unable to negotiate the bureaucracies that society has set up to help or to control them—schools, hospitals, courts, etc. Sometimes they lack money for carfare, a place to drop off their children for an hour or two, or, simply, correct information. More often they do not alone possess the knowledge or power to make these institutions work effectively for them.

Traditionally social workers have tried to help the client build up his ego strength so that he could deal effectively with his life situation. They also gave the client substantive knowledge of how to negotiate his environment, i.e., what his rights were; how to apply for jobs, etc. MFY added a new dimension—a new tool for the client. Today if a lady is having trouble with her welfare investigator, she may very well reply, "If you don't give me my rights, I will tell my MFY social worker." It is not much power, but it is more than she had before. This is a direct result of the advocacy role of the social worker.

Some have argued that the Centers' advocacy has created dependency in clients. While undoubtedly a systematic approach to teaching clients to negotiate the bureaucracies for themselves might have yielded some benefits both materially and psychologically, there simply was not time to do it. In addition, such individual educational efforts would have had little cumulative effect upon the operation of the bureaucracies whose functioning was the problem in the first place.

MFY chose to organize the client consumers of service to advocate and press for the bureaucracies to change their procedures. The results achieved by these organizations clearly point to the value of autonomous client organizations. Until an effective service system is devised for the slum, client organization is needed. In all likelihood, the effective system will not be developed without the prod of client organization.

Nevertheless, while involving clients in the planning and operation of social services is important as a corrective measure to the fads and conceptual errors that crop up periodically among professional planners, such involvement is not to be taken as the sine qua non of effective priority planning. Those who uncritically espouse the currently fashionable idea of "community based programs" overlook the fact that such planning has as many difficulties and problems as professionally based planning. Tomasa Buenaventura may well be asked to serve on an advisory committee for a Neighborhood Service Center, and she may well be representative in the sense of being similar to thousands of other women with like problems. But what way is there for her to communicate with these others, to be responsive to their demands. How can they influence what she says and thinks, how can they act as a corrective to her fads and conceptual errors?

The salient trait of the low-income community is its disorganization or lack of organization. If "the people" or "the community" are really to plan, then they must be organized in groups to make their wishes known through their representatives. At Mobilization this was best done not by setting up planning groups per se and asking people to serve on advisory committees or boards, but through creating organizations like the welfare client groups that provided people with tangible rewards, e.g., increased welfare payments, lower food costs, job training programs, etc. From such groups ultimately came those who organized a campaign to save the Neighborhood Service Centers when their funds were threatened and who will head the boards of the Neighborhood Service Centers soon to be developed independently of Mobilization.

While traditionally professionals have always stated that they wished to turn over policy direction of agencies to local people, this has seldom happened in a real way. One reason for this lack has been the belief that such an event could occur merely by providing the opportunities and without otherwise planning for it. The first step in any plan for local control is the organization of the low-income community. Without such a plan, all that will be accomplished is some combination of professional control and control by unrepresentative groups of local people, neither of whom would be truly accountable or responsive to the community.[4] Those who plan and set priorities must be able to be held accountable for their plans.

Summary

Whatever priorities are set in neighborhoods, perhaps the most significant implication of the MFY experience is that there seems to be a bottomless well of unmet needs for service in the slums. The desire to help is the motivating impulse of social work—this desire is also the greatest threat to its effectiveness. If the profession is not to be trapped in a quagmire of unmet needs (and the client as well), then at times radical approaches must be taken. The object is to make the client "not need" the service.

It must be borne in mind that not all needs can be met through the provision of services. There are needs that people have for self-esteem, for a sense of mastery over their environment. The meeting of these psychological needs is often the prerequisite for alterations in the self-defeating attitudes that prevent many of the slum poor from making use of the available resources. Undoubtedly the civil rights movement has been a source of tremendous psychological help in the slum. With the same end in mind, Mobilization pioneered in the hiring of local people to partially man the Neighborhood Service Centers. It is a difficult question for social workers to ask if there is something more important than good service. Yet in the slum there are times when standards of service may have to be compromised for the psychological gains attendant to local control and staffing.

[4]This is not to say that opportunities should not be made for interested local people even if they do not represent a group in an organized sense. Local people can gain a great deal of experience through such opportunities as well as impart a great deal of important knowledge to professionals in the process.

Radical, in terms of the planning of services, means refusing to set up services on a simplistic notion of *need*. Almost all social services can be justified in slums. Realizing this, agencies must refuse to set up certain services because others promise better results for more people. A well trained "counselor" can help families to be more self-reliant. There is no need to argue this. But, from a great many vantage points as well as that of self-reliance, a neighborhood birth control program would be a more effective service for the slum poor.

The Mobilization experience shows that when an agency sets its priorities in nontraditional ways, it can become an object of controversy and ultimately a political entity.[5] The setting of priorities for social service is, in the broadest and best sense of the word, a political matter. In a democracy the setting of social priorities cannot and should not be taken out of politics even though in the short run the selected priorities may seem shortsighted. Mobilization for Youth's enduring contribution to social welfare may indeed be that it not only pioneered the development of certain innovative social services but also that it preserved the idea through its program priorities that social services must themselves become social issues before the social problems they aim at can be solved.

References

Barr, S. New dimensions in social and medical service for young children: A review of the Mobilization for Youth program. Paper presented at the conference on Changing Patterns of Health Services for Pre-school Children, University of Minnesota, September, 1965.

Beck, B. M. Neighborhood organizations in the delivery of services and self-help. Paper presented at the National Conference on Social Welfare, Dallas, May, 1967.

Berry, M. The contributions of the neighborhood approach in solving today's problems. *Social Service Review*, 1962, *36*, 189–193.

Burgess, E. W. The natural area as the unit for social work in the large city. In *Proceedings, National Conference of Social Work*, Vol. 53. Chicago: University of Chicago Press, 1926. Pp. 504–510.

Cloward, R. A., & Elman, R. M. The storefront on Stanton Street: Advocacy in the ghetto. In G.A. Brager & F. P. Purcell (Eds.), *Community action against poverty*. New Haven: College and University Press, 1967.

Coles, R. Journey into the mind of the low depths. *The New Republic*, February 15, 1964, pp. 11–12.

Harris, J. K. Automating Neighborhood Centers: Potentials and problems. Paper presented at the National Conference on Social Welfare, Dallas, May, 1967.

Mobilization for Youth. *A proposal for the prevention and control of delinquency by expanding opportunities*. New York: MFY, 1961.

[5]The agency was subjected to public attack by the New York *Daily News* and a variety of other interests opposed to its programmatic priority system, welfare client groups, rent strikes, etc.

Chapter 9
An Innovative Treatment Program
for Adolescent Delinquent Boys
Within a Suburban Community

Milton F. Shore
and
Joseph L. Massimo

Although there is much less social disorganization in suburban communities than in inner city slums, it would be inaccurate to assume that suburban areas have no social problems, even though many suburbs sometimes refuse to recognize the existence of problems like delinquency within their midst. The root of these difficulties, however, lies not so much in the social breakdown within the community, but rather in the alienation between the individual, his family, and the large number of resources that are available. A program for delinquents, therefore, must aim at breaking this alienation and facilitating the contacts between the individual and the social structure. In the case of the antisocial youth in suburbia, it means dealing with those intrapsychic and interpersonal elements that have prevented use of the available facilities. In this process constructive forces within the community can be utilized therapeutically. Using the clinical model of ego psychology, Shore and Massimo show how these forces can be mobilized to help those youth who are in trouble with the law.

Chapter 9

An Innovative Treatment Program
for Adolescent Delinquent Boys
Within a Suburban Community

Milton F. Shore
and
Joseph L. Massimo

Newton, Massachusetts, is a middle-class suburb of Boston. According to the 1960 census, it had a population of a little over 90,000, about eight-tenths of 1% of which were nonwhite (these were primarily Negro and Oriental). The median family income was $9,600, as compared with the United States median family income of $5,600, which places it in the top 20% in income in the United States. It has a well-known school system with many experimental educational programs and many mental health personnel within the school, such as psychologists, pupil personnel workers, counselors, and school social workers. The community has relatively few social agencies. It has a small Family Service Association and at the time of this program was planning a mental health center that is now in operation. However, the accessibility of public transportation makes the facilities in the Boston area easily available to Newton residents. For those who are able to afford it, there are a large number of private mental health workers within the city itself.

As with many New England cities, the mobility in Newton is very low. It is seen more as an area of permanent residence for those who have succeeded financially than as a suburb from which one moves on. Unlike many urban areas, the community has an abundance of opportunities—recreational, educational, vocational, etc.—where youth can find activities available.

However, despite the many positive features within the community, there remain problems of delinquency. These problems take forms more typical of middle-class suburban areas—they are directed more against property than people (vandalism and breaking and entering are the most common crimes), and they are handled through many methods alternative to immediate legal processing.

¹This paper is an expansion and elaboration of one originally published in the *Community Mental Health Journal*, Winter 1966, *2, 329–332.*

There is also a difference in those who become delinquent in Newton, a difference again which is typical of many middle-class suburbs. Although many of the delinquents come from the low socioeconomic classes, the families tend to be intact, father is employed full time, and the racial origin is primarily Caucasian. (The nonwhites in suburbia tend to be primarily middle class who have been able to move out of the inner cities.)

For many years the school system had been concerned about these youths who had been doing poorly in school despite all attempts to help them, and who had been in difficulty with the community, especially the legal authorities. These youths would frequently wait until age 16 so that they could leave school on their own, if they had not already been suspended for antisocial activities. The school system of Newton always has had a close relationship to the Judge Baker Guidance Center, a child guidance clinic in the center of Boston. This association led to many joint studies in such areas as learing disturbances in children, school phobias, etc.

Since a primary concern of the school was delinquency, a large pilot study was initiated, funded in part by the National Institute of Mental Health, whose aim was to identify and study the suburban delinquent youth who tended to drop out, and to try to develop new techniques if necessary to meet any needs he might have. This pilot study revealed, among other things, that what these youths needed were multiple services, such as remedial education, psychotherapy, and vocational guidance.

Once these needs were identified, the problem became how best they could be combined and in what fashion they most effectively could be organized to serve these disturbed youths. One such way was to combine all of these services *within one practitioner* who flexibly would offer what was needed at a given time within the realistic setting of employment. This employment program, which was called comprehensive vocationally oriented psychotherapy, has been described in detail previously (Massimo & Shore, 1963, 1967; Shore & Massimo, 1966).

In order to carry out this program, it was necessary to mobilize certain community groups. For example, one of the important aspects of the program was that the youths be seen within 24 hours after leaving school, a time of crisis for these boys. It was felt that approached with the possibility of employment during this crisis period the boy would be most amenable to help, which could then lead to remedial education and psychotherapy, both of which are characteristically rejected by these youths if offered early in the relationship. Because this was an experimental program, it was also important that certain people be aware that only certain members of the group would be given the experimental program, while others would not.

In working with boys with antisocial problems who have been suspended from or dropped out of school, especially if one is planning a program of

employment, one has to deal with three agencies within the community: the
school, legal authorities, and employers.

Schools

The cooperation of the schools in many programs for school dropouts, of
course, is imperative, if only to understand how the school operates or to get
some information about the student and why he dropped out. For this study it
was particularly important that the social structure of the school be understood.
The schools in this suburban community had always been receptive to new
ideas, and the therapist had known the assistant superintendent personally. The
assistant superintendent was able to inform the superintendent of schools himself about the objectives of the program (especially its research elements), the
affiliation of the therapist with a responsible treatment agency, and the nature
of the proposed plan for the boys. He was also a source of information for
understanding of the chain of communication within the school system. The
principals of the high schools were seen to tell them about the program. Then
pupil personnel workers and masters of each of the grade levels (houses) within
the high school were notified personally of the program and its initiation.

The person most important in initiating contact with the boy was the supervisor of attendance and his staff. The attendance officer in some ways is a modern
outgrowth of the old truant officer who has been described in much of the literature on young boys as actively pursuing those who did not attend school. Since
the attendance officer was the first to know when a boy had left school, it was
essential that he understand the program and especially the needs of the therapist, which were to know the name, address, and telephone number of each of
the boys within 24 hours after the boy had dropped out or had been expelled
because of antisocial behavior and academic failure. It was necessary to make
clear the criteria of selection of the boys (15 to 17 years old, average IQ, and no
overt evidence of either psychosis or brain damage). The attendance officer also
had to be told that although some 20 boys would be contacted, only 10 would be
given the program. The reasons for the control group were explained in detail.

The boy who had left school was legally the responsibility of the attendance
officer unless the parents agreed in writing to assume this responsibility
(none of the parents agreed to do so). This responsibility ended when the boy
became 16 years of age. Under the age of 16 the boy was legally required to
report to the attendance officer, who planned a program for him. In point of
fact, because of his large load, it was difficult for the attendance officer to
keep tabs on the boys. Under the age of 16 this meant checking to see that the
boy did not leave home during school hours without special permission. It was
important that the attendance officer realize that those boys who were not being

actively engaged in treatment could receive the services normally available to individuals who left school.

The therapist made clear that he would not ask the school for any special requests, nor was he active with school personnel in any way other than trying to gain their cooperation. He was permitted to gather information from the school files and any background information from the supervisor of attendance and the counselors that would help him in dealing with the boy. At no point did he urge the boys to return to school unless they were eager to do so.

The school personnel were very eager and enthusiastic about the program and especially that someone was attempting a new approach with these youths, since they had been extremely troublesome within the school setting. At the same time, having used all available school resources without success, the school was often relieved when the boy decided to leave.

Frequent informal contacts with the supervisor of attendance kept him informed as to the progress of the program, especially with those boys who were under 16 years of age and, therefore, still legally the responsibility of the educational system.

There were no problems with gaining the cooperation of the schools. Since the community was the focus of the program, little feedback on each boy to the schools took place except when the boy had decided to return to school (four boys at one time or another chose to do so). At that point there was a discussion between the worker, the principal, and the counselors about the specific boy and the problems that might arise.

Despite the minimal feedback on each boy, the success of the program had considerable influence in the school and led to an expansion of counseling programs for delinquent youth. The counselors, eager to read about the total program, have discussed the possibilities of a large work-study-counseling program in the schools, a discussion that recently culminated in a proposal for funding a special program based on the principles of comprehensive vocationally oriented psychotherapy. Also one of the colleges in the area has been interested in a similar study with girls.

Employers

Most important in any vocationally oriented program is work with the employment areas of the community. There were two aims in such work—one was to collect a pool of opportunities for employment, the second to make certain the experience would be constructive for the boy and could lead to building in a variety of other services that the boys so desperately needed but could not accept. It was clear from the beginning, however, that although employers needed some sensitivity and tolerance, they could not be expected to play the role of therapist with the boys but should be viewed as being able to offer a reality situation around which other services such as remedial education and psychotherapy could be offered by the therapist when needed.

The strategy for approaching employers was initiated by writing both the governor of the state and the head of the Department of Labor in the state describing the need for new programs and the nature of the planned program in detail. Both wrote back expressing interest and encouragement, with the Department of Labor showing particular interest, and stating they would support such efforts in any way possible. They both also expressed the hope that the necessary cooperation from civic-minded employers would be forthcoming.

In order to obtain a pool of jobs, the therapist spoke before the Chamber of Commerce, Rotary Club, and many executive groups as well as to individual employers, describing the importance of the project in helping these boys become useful citizens. One civic-minded employer who had for many years prided himself on the fact that he had employed ex-convicts successfully was especially helpful in suggesting other employers in the community who would be sympathetic to the idea. He also helped in describing ways of approaching these employers so as not to threaten them.

Some of the problems an employer might encounter with these boys were described by the therapist. The therapist told the prospective employers that the boys were on probation and had been in trouble in the school and community but that they were not psychotic. He promised to help the boy with his educational problems, his job performance, and his attitude and would be available to assist the employer at any time the employer found it necessary to call him. He did not expect the employer to coddle the boys in any way. The therapist also spoke about the boys in terms of their low threshold for anger and how the employer might handle situations that could arise. The employer's self-interest was constantly emphasized: each employer would in the end be helping himself if a young person were prevented from becoming an expense to the taxpayer. (One must remember that the community in which the work was carried out was a suburban middle-class community where social responsibility was seen as a virtue. There were also many jobs available, although these boys were alienated from the informational resources, as well as unable to follow through if given an opportunity for employment.) As a result of these discussions with the therapist, some employers listened intently and stated they did not want to hire the boys, while others stated that they might hire the boy if he made no false move. Still others were anxious but eager to give it a try. After obtaining a list of jobs, the therapist saw each employer individually if there was any chance that a boy might be placed with him. This permitted the employer to back out if he was too uncomfortable, and also helped the therapist in determining if the employer was suitable for the boy.

However, the largest number of jobs were not obtained from talks but rather from personal trips to likely business establishments (such as automobile deal-ers) where the therapist saw the owner, described the program, and asked for other employers who might hire one of the boys. In discussing the situation with each of the employers, the therapist was aware of the labor laws of the state as well as issues of salary and insurance. For example, because of the nature of the machines in the company and the labor laws of the state, some establishments could not hire boys under the age of 18, some had restrictions on the hours of employment of such youths, and some could not hire individuals with question-able backgrounds because of the fear of potential danger either to themselves or to other employees.

It was emphasized to each employer that under no circumstances was he required to keep a boy who was not able to perform up to the standards required by the company. In fact, it was up to the employer to select a particular boy. As a result, some firms decided not to hire the first boy who arrived to be interviewed for the position.

Understanding the anxieties related to being interviewed for a position and realizing the possibility that the boy might be turned down for the job, the ther-apist always accompanied the boy to the job interview. This way the boy was not only prepared for the interview but was able to receive the support necessary for handling the frustration of perhaps being denied something he wanted—a therapeutic experience in itself. If this happened, the therapist and the boy dis-cussed the situation and proceeded to look for other employment opportunities. The boys had the opportunity to see how one talks to a boss and how one han-dles frustration and searches in other directions.

Within five months the therapist had collected a pool of 60 job opportunities for the 10 boys who would be in the treatment program. However, since a major aspect of the program was to tie the job closely to the boy's ability, training, and personality needs, there were still times when the kinds of jobs the therapist knew about met few of the boy's needs. It was then that the boy and the thera-pist thought about what jobs would be most appropriate and through want ads or word-of-mouth were able to find positions which they explored together. For example, the therapist and the boy were able to find a job with a wrecking firm for a youth who had had very little control over his primitive destructive impulses. This opportunity to work with others in destroying buildings served as a very successful outlet for the primitive, destructive drives.

One arrangement that was made with the employer was that the therapist wished to maintain contact with the boy and would like to visit the place of employment at least every two weeks if the boy wished. (Some boys did not want the therapist to see them on the job but were eager to see the therapist either before or after work.) Through the contacts with the employer and the boy, the therapist was able to get a picture of what was going on on the job from both points of view. Although using the information himself, he did not in any way share information from either of these sources with the other. Even though the employer was asked not to give special consideration to the boy who was causing trouble, it was noticed that their eagerness to participate in the program often raised the employer's threshold for deviance. The therapist also protected the boy against undue exploitation by the employer. In one case, for example, the boy was urged to leave the job and seek another because the employer was clearly attempting to take advantage of him. The therapist also helped the boys when they sought to advance from one job to another.

One agreement between the therapist and the employer was that if the boy had any difficulty the employer was to call the therapist so that the situation could be handled immediately with the boy. In two cases where the boys were fired because of stealing, the therapist was able to sit with the boy and the employer and find out specifically what had happened and what issues were involved.

Employment served to make the boys aware of some of their difficulties so that other kinds of assistance became necessary. For example, discovering that one of the boys could not read, his fellow workers attempted to scapegoat the boy by forcing him to read the labels on oil cans. The boy burst into a fit of rage. The therapist knew of the boy's deficiency but felt that the boy, who was also aware of this lack although he did not want to accept it, had to experience its implications directly. The therapist was called immediately and worked with the boy around setting up a remedial reading program as well as helping the boy learn to handle the provocation of fellow workers in such a way as to not get himself into trouble.

Two major problems arose with regard to employment and needed to be worked out. Some labor unions were concerned that these youths would take jobs away from adults who were in greater need of employment. After the boy was hired the union would either approach him to join or in some way express dissatisfaction. The boy's therapist worked with the employer, whose knowledge of the labor unions was great; and he was always able to work out in some way an arrangement with the union whereby the boy could remain on the job.

The greatest difficulty, however, came from the state employment service. They made quite clear that they would have nothing to do with a program which did not in anyway urge, cajole, or pressure the boys to return to school. They refused to share any of their knowledge of employment possibilities in the community. They refused to assist in the vocational testing of the boys. Since the program was not dependent upon state employment services, no attempts were made to work with them. They were ignored. Although refusing to cooperate, at no point did the state employment service in any way actively impair, impede, or block the implementation of the program.

Law Enforcement System

In treating antisocial individuals, contacts with controlling authorities such as police became inevitable. In this program, as with the job, legal authorities were seen as a reality with which the boys had to deal. The therapist called the boy's probation officer and discussed with him his plans for the boy. He explained that the program would help the boy with work and his problems at home. He also described the research design. These officers expressed a great interest and, especially because of their large caseloads, were eager to have someone assume part of the responsibility for the boys. The therapist knew some of the policemen socially. He also had met a group of policemen when he came down to bail out one of the boys at 4:00 a.m. one morning. The police got to know the therapist as someone eagerly desiring to help young people. Informally, the therapist also kept the probation officers posted on what was happening to the boys.

The problems with the police were minor and limited to individual policemen. Although most of the police saw the therapist as offering a valuable alternative to legal measures, some were discouraged and felt that nothing other than severe punishment would help the boys. However, they were able to accept the idea that a new approach was worth a try and were especially pleased that they were not asked to give special privileges or urged to change their attitudes. It was generally felt that the outcome of the program was to be its most effective technique for attitude change. Many policemen were indeed pleased by the successful results and expressed personal satisfaction with the changes in many of the boys.

Summary

The aims of this program were clear—to facilitate the carrying out of a small experimental treatment program based on principles derived from a clinical model.

The program itself was not generated from the community, nor did it require large-scale community planning. It was a program, however, that attempted to deal with a major community problem—the high school dropout who is in trouble with the law. The fact that certain aspects of the community could be successfully mobilized around the implementation of such a program was essential to the program's success in treating youths usually considered "unreachable" by the resources available within suburban schools or agencies.

References

Massimo, J. L., & Shore, M. F. The effectiveness of a vocationally oriented psychotherapy program for adolescent delinquent boys. *American Journal of Orthopsychiatry*, 1963, *33*, 634–643. Reprinted in F. Riessman, J. Cohen, & A. Pearl (Eds.), *Mental health of the poor.* Glencoe, Ill.: The Free Press, 1965.

Massimo, J. L., & Shore, M. F. Comprehensive vocationally oriented psychotherapy: A new treatment technique for lower class adolescent delinquent youth. *Psychiatry*, 1967, *30*, 229–236.

Shore, M. F., & Massimo, J. L. Comprehensive vocationally oriented psychotherapy for adolescent delinquent boys: A follow-up study. *American Journal of Orthopsychiatry*, 1966, *36*, 609–616.

Part IV
New Areas

While many programs are either related to specific social issues, tied to generally outlined service structures, or directed toward certain symptom groups, mental health professionals are also venturing into new areas that have major mental health implications but that have no history or tradition upon which to fall back. They require the adaptation and integration of existing knowledge in new directions. One of these areas involves changing certain aspects of the employment structure of society so as to create new jobs and train people for new positions. The "New Careers" program described in this section is of special significance since automation has eliminated many jobs that traditionally went to less skilled individuals. The development of new jobs means working with the employment structure toward changing some of the basic principles and assumptions upon which present practice is based.

Another area, and one of the most exciting challenges to mental health workers, is their involvement in the early phases of planning new communities. Different from those programs aimed toward changing existing structures, this area may been seen as one of the basic directions in which community mental health principles can be put into practice—the area of the prevention of mental illness and the promotion of social competence. The ultimate measure of the effectiveness of our community mental health ideas may indeed lie in what happens in these new planned communities when suggestions made by mental health experts are properly implemented. The experience of one mental health consultant who was involved in such planning is described in this section.

Chapter 10
New Careers:
Program Development and the
Process of Institutional Change

Beryce W. MacLennan

The recent concern with the mental health of the poor has led to the revival of interest in the role meaningful work plays in the psychological functioning of the individual. Shore and Massimo, in their chapter, have described how employment could be used as a tool for psychotherapeutic intervention in lower-class adolescents living in suburbia. However, the implications of work programs for individuals of all ages, especially the poor in the inner city, go far beyond that of only a strategy for intervention. While unskilled jobs in industry are becoming fewer and fewer in number, society has become aware of new areas of need. These areas are those of the human service fields, which include teacher aides and community workers. But the use of this area requires changes in the employment structure as presently conceived and constructed. What changes needed to occur and how they were brought about in Washington, D.C., is described by Dr. MacLennan.

Chapter 10

New Careers:
Program Development and the
Process of Institutional Change

Beryce W. MacLennan

The analysis and reorganization of tasks, in order to make the most effective use of the knowledge, skill, experience, and character possessed by the labor force, is not new. Indeed, it was at the heart of the industrial revolution and made possible the tremendous increase in productivity over the last 150 years. Nor is such practice particularly new in human service. The nursing profession in the 1940's and 1950's reorganized and created positions for nurses' aides, practical nurses, and R. N.'s requiring different degrees of skill and knowledge (Lee, 1958). The Armed Forces, possessing a quantity of manpower with a wide range of capacity and education, has always deployed its forces in this way. In the late 1950's and 1960's, a number of people experimented with using nonprofessionals in human service either as ancillary manpower (Riessman, 1963; Rioch, Elkes, & Flint, 1965; Weed & Denham, 1961) or as a rehabilitative measure (Grant, 1965). The correctional field has always been largely staffed by nonprofessionals. What is new is that channels for employment and advancement should be created *and* means for self-support provided, so that individuals with limited education and originally no skills, training, or financial resources can systematically be hired as nonprofessionals and can become technical assistants and full professionals if they have the ability and the desire.

The essence of New Careers is entry into the system without prior qualification and the creation and institutionalization of machinery and support for upward mobility (Center for Youth and Community Studies, 1965; MacLennan, 1964; Pearl & Riessman, 1965). This machinery and support must include not only well-defined positions for advancement within institutions but also the opportunity for continuing education and training and the financial support that enables poor people to take advantage of such opportunities.

The New Careers approach, however, can only become a reality if considerable changes are made in the present functioning of employment and educational institutions. This demand for institutional changes was not originally clearly understood but became apparent as programs developed.

The Howard University New Careers Training Program

The New Careers program at Howard University was developed and primarily implemented by the staff of the Training Center for the Control and Prevention of Juvenile Delinquency and Youth Crime.[1] The program was stimulated by two different needs. One was the shortage of personnel to work in the rehabilitation of delinquents and in human services generally. The staff thought that the only largely unexploited and undeveloped pool of potential talent in the country was the disadvantaged groups of society and particularly poor youth, and that it might be possible to reorganize professional work to make jobs for them.

The other need was to find new ways to prevent and control delinquency. Cloward and Ohlin (1960) had recently propounded the theory that a major cause of delinquency was the alienation of large segments of society because they were excluded from the opportunity to benefit from the material and prestige systems of the country. This exclusion seemed to arise through a lack of qualifications to enter employment and for employment advancement. They stated that youth excluded in this way created their own antisocial society with its own status system. Consequently, they believed that it would be necessary to provide opportunities for all people within the larger society in order to reduce the attraction of the deviant system.

The Howard University group planned to meet both these needs by the development of New Careers in Human Service fields. If jobs and opportunities for advancement for poor youth who were out of school and out of work could be created, and if training in human relations and work skills could be provided, it might be possible to reduce alienation and delinquency. At the same time, the mandate of the Office of Juvenile Delinquency Training Center to train personnel and to increase resources for the control and prevention of juvenile delinquency and youth crime would be accomplished through the employment of the youth in human service fields (Center for Youth and Community Studies, 1965; MacLennan, 1964).

It was known that professionals were forced to undertake many tasks that did not require a high degree of education and training, tasks that they might be only too glad to surrender to others less highly qualified than themselves. Therefore, if professional responsibilities could be reorganized and many of the simpler tasks detached and assembled into new technical jobs, the professional would be relieved and the service made more efficient. Also, professional background and training, with its emphasis on emotional detachment, expertapplicant relationship, and frequent lack of intimate knowledge and contact with the culture of poverty, did not easily permit the management of situations requiring a man-to-man equalitarian approach. Consequently, it was thought

[1]Office of Juvenile Delinquency and Youth Crime (OJDYC).

that there were times when a youth or a neighborhood worker could be more effective than a professional.

This essentially pointed up the third innovative aspect of New Careers in the human service fields (the first being upward mobility; the second, entry without prior qualifications)—that is, the importance of all staff members as change-agents, the respect for the nonprofessional point of view in planning and decision-making, and the consequent reduction of distance and increase in communication between different staff levels.

Because the New Careers idea was novel and there was sure to be distrust of the reliability of out-of-work, out-of-school, poor youth, it was planned first to train a small number of aides in specially created field placements, two of which were within the Center's own operations and one in a nearby nonprofit day-care center. This would test whether the youth could perform successfully in this kind of work. It was then planned to introduce them to jobs funded by demonstration monies in the Washington Action for Youth (WAY), a delinquency prevention community action program in Washington, D.C., to refine training methods. This period of demonstration would also give lead time to persuade the administrators of private and public service institutions in health, education, welfare, and recreation that this was a feasible solution to some of their manpower problems and to work with them and with personnel toward the creation and funding of permanent positions. Once jobs and training at the entry level were satisfactorily designed, it would then be possible to consider their institutionalization and move to the development and accreditation of continuing education and training at the associate of arts and bachelor levels or through diploma and certification courses.

An initial research demonstration contract from the National Institutes of Health[2] was obtained in early 1964, which was combined with OJDYC Training Center funds to train 10 aides in day care, recreation, and research. Very soon after, the staff wrote and began to negotiate a contract with the Office of Manpower, Automation, and Training (OMAT) in the Labor Department and the Office of Education (OE) to develop an Aide Training Center and to train 200 aides and 40 subprofessional youth trainers and supervisors to work in the WAY program. Subprofessional training was included as well as aide training because with the passing of the Economic Opportunities Act and the creation of the Office of Economic Opportunity (OEO), there would predictably be a tremendous shortage of youth leaders, counselors, trainers, and because even without OEO programs, it was hard to obtain suitable training staff. The training of subprofessional youth trainers would also begin to create a model for the associate of arts program or technical certificate, which was seen as a next step in the development of educational opportunity.

Before the initial three-month training program was completed in the early

[2]NIH Contract No. 3T1–MH–8318–0381.

summer of 1964, organizational changes had occurred in the demonstration program. WAY had been incorporated in the District of Columbia community action planning organization (UPO). The original training center and jobs for aides were never to be created, and it was immediately necessary to negotiate with the traditional agencies two years ahead of schedule for jobs for the trainees and for positions that would justify the contract with OMAT, which was expected momentarily. (It took a year to negotiate complete funding with administrative money received in January and training funds in June, 1965.) This was a particularly difficult contract to negotiate because it combined funds from different sources and because the on-the-job aspects might require matching funds from the District of Columbia (D.C.) and might reduce the amount of Federal money the D.C. Employment Service could hope to obtain for other work-training programs. They were, therefore, somewhat unwilling to approve an independent program.

Because of the criteria for entry positions demanded by the institutions, the question of skill and educational qualifications became immediately a crucial issue. There were almost no entry positions in existence under a GS-4.[1] While Civil Service regulations stated that individuals could be hired with minimal educational qualifications provided they had three years experience, candidates could not obtain the experience without educational qualifications, generally two years of college, and written examinations.

By the spring of 1964, the staff had begun to realize that in order to achieve their goal, massive changes in institutional structure and functioning would be necessary (MacLennan, Klein, Pearl & Fishman, 1966). Task allocation, job definitions, and hiring practices had to be reorganized within the human service agencies. Agency boards, Civil Service, union and professional associations had to be persuaded to accept and authenticate the changes. Legislation had to be written and passed to approve and fund the positions. A new philosophy of education and training had to be advanced. This stated that the individual should start work with minimal preparations, but that opportunity for fully accredited education and training should be built into the job so that any aide could advance if he had the ability, energy, and interest, to professional and administrative positions. Thus, the poor as well as the rich would have access to a career. Entry training, continuing inservice staff development, new kinds of associate of arts and bachelor programs, training of instructors, supervisors, trainers would have to be promoted and the impact of these changes on the education and training of the professional examined. A massive job of reorgani-

[1]The G.S. classification system in civil service is based on educational qualifications, training, and length and quality of experience. Career lines may go from GS-1 to GS-15 or start and stop at any intermediate grade. Positions are graded by means of job descriptions and carry salaries commensurate with the grade. Promotion and salary increases can be accorded through step advances within the grade as well as from grade to grade. At the time when these programs were being developed, a GS-2 was paid $3,600; and a GS-6 somewhere around $5,800.

zation, innovation, and above all persuasion had to be tackled. At the present time (fall, 1967) reports are being circulated of the creation of many positions, new educational programs, and legislation. Professional committees are examining the impact of these changes on the work and training of professionals. However, it may be worthwhile to examine the early stages of this movement, for movement it has been, with its supporters forced to combine scientific and professional roles with those of evangelist, salesman, and social actionist. Professionals engaged in these programs have had in fact to face an identity change and to add many new skills to their repertoire. They have had to study organizational structures and funding mechanisms, learn how to write a wide variety of job descriptions, become lobbyists and propagandists, understand political maneuvering and the management of pressure groups. They have had to become clearly cognizant of the dimension of power in regard to program development.

Job Negotiation and Institutional Change

In order to understand the problems inherent in negotiating budgeted positions in public service agencies, it is necessary to understand the allocation of decision-making in government and the steps that have to be taken before such positions can be approved. The District of Columbia presented special complications through its relationship to the Federal Government and its dependence on the Federal Government for its appropriations. Thus, permanent positions and funding not only had to be approved by the personnel divisions and administrators of each agency and by the District personnel department and the D.C. Commissioners, but had also to gain the sanction of the Federal Civil Service Commission and run the gamut of the House and Senate D.C. Health, Education, and Welfare and Appropriations Committees. Furthermore, because the District of Columbia is dependent on Federal funding, legislation pertaining to the District is seen as possibly creating precedents for the nation.

Because the concern was not only with the immediate creation of temporary jobs but also with the design and funding of permanent career lines, staff had to become familiar with the construction of organizational charts, job descriptions, the leeways and limitations of budget manipulation, and to recognize that budgets are planned one and one-half to two years ahead and are finally set in the fall of one year, to be implemented in a July-to-July fiscal year starting nine months later. In September, 1964, preliminary decisions had already been made regarding the detailed budgets for the year July, 1965–July, 1966, and would have to be revised to accommodate human service aides for that year. Meantime, there was relatively little free money for expansions or changes. It was learned that in some agencies unexpended staff funds could be transferred and that unfilled positions, for example two GS-6's might, with the consent of all concerned, be written down and expanded into three GS-2's or GS-3's on a temporary basis. It was also found that certain kinds of money for part-time and temporary staff could be used with greater flexibility for the immediate creation of jobs and that the Civil Service Commission and agency personnel departments recognized the principle of "an exception" to the rules and regulations. Consequently, under certain conditions entry qualifications could be altered or waived, but only on an individual basis. While these mechanisms offered possibilities for immediate jobs, they would not serve to create authenticated, budgeted and funded, permanent positions necessary for the development of career lines.

Thus, in the summer of 1964, senior training staff found themselves involved in a massive job development program and forced to consider new areas and learn new skills quite foreign to their ordinary lives as mental health professionals.

Each institution had its own special problems. Most easily negotiated were positions in a new Day Care Association, a private, nonprofit organization paid for originally by community action funds but sponsored by the Health and Welfare Council. Here a hierarchy of job positions could be described and written into the program, starting with nonprofessional aides through technical teachers' assistants to fully qualified teaching, supervisory, and administrative positions. Job descriptions, training procedures, and selection of trainees were worked out jointly between Howard and the agency staff, who also participated in the training (Bloomberg & Klein, 1965).

Public Welfare in the District of Columbia has responsibility for relief, AFDC, and protective programs, and for the conduct of institutions for children and the aged. The Welfare director and deputy director in charge of institutions were approached and were interested because they had a high turnover among their institutional counselors and pre-school nursing staffs and had a large number of vacancies. These staff started as GS-4's, entry requirements for which were two years of college or three years of experience. Most staff were working to complete college and to obtain master's degrees. They then left to find more lucrative and rewarding employment. A variety of alternatives were discussed. If staff could be introduced at lower grades and educational levels, they could be trained to be effective staff members and, through combined education and staff development, could rise within the system, thus reducing turnover. Because the District institutions are Federally financed, there was a need to find Federal precedents. Most desirable would be to create GS-2 and GS-3 Institutional Counselor Aide positions, which could then feed into a GS-4 Counselor career line; but such positions would have to be passed by the District of Columbia government and by the Civil Service Commission, all of which would take time. Already existing Teachers' Aides positions, GS-2, were found in the Bureau of Indian Affairs, which might be adapted to the needs of the program; and positions for Nurses' Aides, GS-2 and GS-3, were already in existence although unfilled and unbudgeted. This involved discussions with the Welfare administrators and personnel officers, the D.C. personnel officer, and the Federal Civil Service Commission about the reorganization of positions and budget. It also necessitated the willingness of administrators to redistribute budget. It meant talks with the Welfare training officer regarding the training of the aides and with unit administrators and professional supervisors regarding the development of new job descriptions and the reorganization of previous responsibilities. Orientation of supervisory personnel to the goals of the program and to the characteristics and needs of the trainees had to be undertaken. Eventually it was possible to add temporary GS-2 and GS-3 Institutional Counselor Aide positions at the bottom of the counselor career line. These aides had to possess at least high school equivalency to be eligible (Felsenfeld, 1967).

One problem in introducing aides into fields such as welfare, recreation, and day care was that many of the workers and some supervisors had entered on the strength of a college degree but had received little or no specific training. Consequently, they sometimes knew less than the aides had learned at the end of their basic training (MacLennan, 1966). It was essential either to organize intensive inservice training or to arrange appropriate educational seminars and skill workshops with some local university or training institution. These matters had to be worked out with the agency training and staff development officers. However, it did not always obviate the friction that occurred naturally when aides trained in modern methods were placed under old-line staff who had evolved their own ways of dealing with difficult situations.

In the D.C. Recreation Department, with the strong support of the Neighborhood Centers Division and the Roving Leaders (detached workers), it was possible to allocate funds and to change entry qualifications for temporary positions paid for on a per diem basis and ultimately to develop a collaborative program with the Neighborhood Youth Corps program, which could pay the aides during the entry training and work experience phase. Initially, a proposal was written, and an unsuccessful attempt was made to obtain funds for an innovative Neighborhood Center recreation demonstration which, joined with training center funds, could have provided aides with training and full-time positions at GS-2 and GS-3 levels on an experimental basis. The department was willing to guarantee that if the aides were satisfactory, the positions would be incorporated in the permanent budget and form continuity with the regular career line which ordinarily started at GS-4. Even though this plan did not work out, it was possible later to initiate a training program for recreation aides; and aides are now permitted to count per diem work as experience toward qualifying for permanent agency positions.

A new multidisciplinary position of hospital extension home care aide was discussed with the Health Department (Klein & MacLennan, 1965). It was conceived that this kind of aide would be trained in a variety of simple tasks drawn from the duties of the nurse, homemaker, occupational and physical therapist, and would visit homebound and convalescent patients to carry out a care program designed by the professionals on the team. From this position, the aide could move into any of the four professional streams as further education and training were made available. Distrust of young workers and problems related to the coordination of supervision prevented the implementation of this program.

It has generally proved simpler to add a lower grade to an already existing Civil Service line than to create an entirely new career line. However, in the United Planning Organization Neighborhood Development Centers, a hierarchy of neighborhood workers was created within which individuals could move from low-level entry jobs to supervisory and administrative positions by virtue of inservice training, experience, and demonstrated competence without formal education (Denham, Walker, & Gross, 1965; Kestenbaum, 1966). A central problem in this program was that jobs had to be described and training implemented before the project was fully developed. The role of the worker changed during training from an emphasis on making connections between people and services to community organization so that the original training quickly became dysfunctional and had to be redesigned for the second and third centers.

Independently organized community action programs presented no immediate problems with regard to funded positions, for here positions could be created overnight. For instance, while waiting for the OMAT-OE training funds, it was possible to combine administrative funds, Juvenile Delinquency training funds, the Neighborhood Youth Corps work experience stipends to train Research Aides for newly created positions in the community action program evaluation (Davis, 1966). However, it has to be recognized that such experiments carry no guarantees of permanency, of future employment or advancement for the aides, and that the positions can be abolished at a day's notice.

Demonstration programs linked to traditional nonprofit organizations such as the Urban League or the Family Service Association are in a better position. When aide and technical assistant positions are created in these agencies, they set a precedent and provide experiences that may well be institutionalized even if the special funds dry up. Once the agency or the Community Chest organization—in the District of Columbia, the United Givers Fund —acknowledges such positions as Casework Aide or Employment Counseling Aide, it is easier to obtain funding for them in the future.

Self-contained programs provide the quickest opportunity for the establishment of a vertical system. For instance, a private residential school system for physically handicapped and brain-damaged children in Aberdeen, Scotland, trains some of the children to become teaching aides and eventually teachers in its own schools. However, these teachers may not be able to teach elsewhere. Only to the extent that the organization is recognized by the larger society and its training accepted can these teachers have horizontal mobility into other organizations.

Where the larger states have espoused the New Careers idea, either in part or in whole, large-scale development of new positions have been made possible—in California within the correctional department, in Pennsylvania in the health and welfare system, and in the youth development programs of New York State.

Efforts to develop teachers' aide and assistant positions within the D.C. school system produced other kinds of problems. One was related to the fact that there were on-going projects and demonstrations with a variety of ideas about what aides should do and who should be aides. Although many aides were employed—at one time at least 300—there was originally no official position and no guarantee of permanency. By the end of 1965, an official position as Teachers' Aide at a GS-2 level, which established entry with minimal qualifications along with conditions for advancement to Teachers' Assistant and eventually Teacher, had been approved. However, in 1966 a Teachers' Salary Amendment Act, passed by the House, limited the employment of teachers' aides to those who had 60 hours of college credit and to a mere 5 percent of the total teaching staff, thus curtailing drastically the possibilities for experimentation within the school system and eliminating the fruits of ongoing research and training.

This emphasized again that, when attempting to effect institutional change, attention has to be paid to all those who have power or influence on that change. In the institutionalization of aides, it has been necessary to gain acceptance from supervisors, administrators, agency personnel departments, city, county, state, and Federal Civil Service organizations, institutional boards, mayors' offices, legislators, and, of course, professional associations who are interested parties influential in supporting or opposing the reorganization of their work.

Throughout the development of the aide programs, staff spent much time interpreting the New Careers idea to local and regional professional groups, reporting on the program at national meetings and writing professional papers.

Education

Initially, none of the aides had graduated from high school so that for the experimental population this was a primary hurdle. Two ways of overcoming this presented themselves. One was to prepare the youth for the high school equivalency exams; the other was to obtain credit for the program as essentially vocational education at the high school level. Howard University agreed to grant a certificate to those who graduated from the program successfully, but this did not affect the need for a high school diploma. Remedial education was provided, and a number of the aides followed the former route and took the examination. In 1966, in collaboration with the D.C. Board of Education, it proved possible to develop a demonstration work, education, and training program within the senior year of high school in which the students were paid on a part-time basis out of Neighborhood Youth Corps funds.

This latter model begins to approximate a central tenet of New Careers: that the educational opportunity should be included within the employment package with time allowed and paid for education and training. In spite of the urgings of Walter Wallace (1965), there is no evidence that the American public is willing to provide subsistence and scholarships for students on any large scale; and ways have to be found so that people can study, earn a living, and support a family without undue stress. If such means are not provided, then channels for advancement are unusable except by those with exceptional energy and determination. It is just too hard for most people, particularly if they have already established a family, to struggle through high school, college, and a master's program on a night-school schedule. The linking of education, training, and employment together as one integral unit, paid for as a job, seems the most feasible solution. In such a model, there is close collaboration between educational centers and employers; and the three components are welded into a functional whole, each aiding in the professional development of the individual. Agency representatives are included in curriculum planning. Credit is allowed for work experience, and work supervisors and trainers are considered as part of the educational faculty. This kind of model is envisioned for entry training, for programs at the associate of arts level, which permit free entry but hold to a firm standard for graduation, for bachelor of arts, and for professional programs.

Quite a few programs have been started at the associate of arts level, and there has been considerable experimentation with time blocks. In some programs, students work half-time and go to school half-time. In others, they have a "training day" a week (Riessman, 1967). In the Einstein program, Levin (1967) suggests several different possibilities. In general, the bachelors' programs are still uninfluenced and remain primarily academic, although a few schools, such as Antioch, have had work and study programs—for instance, in teacher training—for a number of years. Probably the most comprehensive program to date is that developed by Levin at Einstein, in which he carried health service personnel up three career lines from high school to the professional level.

A second trend more in evidence in the Community Action Programs is to bypass the formal academic world altogether and to concentrate on career ladders established within the employing system. However, as Henderson (1965) pointed out, there is considerable likelihood of such a model finding a ceiling at the top of the technician stage and failing to break the professional barrier. Furthermore, it is harder to obtain general acceptance and to achieve mobility across the country.

In some ways, New Careers already creates a difficulty for the professional in that, as has been pointed out, aides and assistants readily acquire in some areas as much or more skill and experience than beginning professionals; and the reorganization of the work makes much greater demands on the professional to do a truly professional job. However, if, in the future, it is possible to implement the paid work experience, education, and training program from aide to professional, the latter, even when newly qualified, would have immeasurably more experience and skill than he possesses today.

These factors will require a total redesigning of professional education, a task that is already being faced in some human service fields (MacLennan, 1967). Here, again, it is necessary to engage in community organization and the stimulation of social change, this time through membership in professional training and manpower committees and consultations to universities and to special commissions established to study such trends.

In summary, the New Careers idea has provided stimulation for massive social change. In order to implement it, it has been and continues to be necessary to work with human service personnel at all levels—supervisors, administrators, professional associations. It has been necessary to involve Civil Service personnel divisions and employment standard setting groups, executives, and legislators. It has become clear that if barriers are to be overcome, new educational models must be designed that make it possible for anyone, whether rich or poor, to take advantage of such training if he has the ability and desire to do so. Consequently, the New Careers professional has had to broaden his skills and knowledge and has to adopt additional roles of lobbyist and salesman. He has had to become more clearly aware of the effects of money and power and to give consideration as to where he must place himself most strategically in order to achieve his goals. He has become, in fact, a political animal and an agent of social change. In such a role, it must be recognized that conflict is inevitable. Change cannot occur without a clash of interests, without resistance and counterpressure. People are threatened by having to take on new roles and learn new tasks. They are afraid that their vested interests will be disturbed. Each situation has to be analyzed in terms of understanding the dynamic pressures likely to be created and strategies for working them out must be devised.

References

Bloomberg, C., & Klein, W. L. *Day care aide training curriculum.* Washington, D.C.: Center for Community Studies, 1965.

Center for Youth and Community Studies. *Training for new careers.* Washington, D.C.: Presidents's Commission on Juvenile Delinquency and Youth Crime, 1965.

Cloward, R. A., & Ohlin, L. E. *Opportunity and delinquency: A theory of delinquent gangs.* Glencoe, Ill.: The Free Press, 1960.

Davis, M. *Neighborhood Youth Corps training programs.* Washington, D.C.: Center for Youth and Community Studies, 1966.

Denham, W. H., Walker, W., & Gross, J. *Training program for neighborhood workers.* Washington, D.C.: UPO Neighborhood Development Center #1, Center for Youth and Community Studies, 1965.

Felsenfeld, N. *New careers in social service: Training for counseling positions in residential programs for children and youth.* Washington, D.C.: Institute for Youth Studies, 1967.

Grant, D. A strategy for new careers development. In A. Pearl & F. Riessman (Eds.), *New Careers for the Poor.* New York: Free Press, 1965, Pp. 209–238.

Henderson, D. M. *New careers: Some analytical remarks.* Washington, D.C.: Center for Youth and Community Studies, 1965.

Kestenbaum, S. *Training for neighborhood workers.* Washington, D.C.: UPO, 1966.

Kestenbaum, S. *Urban service aides training program.* Washington, D.C.: Washington Center for Urban Studies, 1967.

Klein, W. L., & MacLennan, B. W. *Health aide curriculum.* Washington, D.C.: Center for Youth and Community Studies, 1965.

Lee, A. N. The training of non-professional personnel. *Nursing Outlook,* 1958, *6,* 222–225.

Levin, T. *Proposal for the establishment of a division of community education and careers.* New York: Albert Einstein College of Medicine, Lincoln Hospital Mental Health Services, 1967.

MacLennan, B. W. Training for new careers. Paper presented at Conference on Ways Out of Poverty for Disadvantaged Youth, Howard University, Washington, D.C., 1964.

MacLennan, B. W. *Counseling in the field of corrections.* Prepared for the D.C. Joint Commission on Correctional Manpower and Training, 1967.

MacLennan, B. W., Klein, W. L., Pearl, A., & Fishman, J. Training for new careers. *Community Mental Health Journal,* 1966, *2,* 135–141.

Pearl, A., & Riessman, F. *New careers for the poor.* New York: Free Press, 1965.

Riessman, F. *The revolution in social work: The new non-professsional.* New York: Mobilization for Youth, 1963.

Riessman, F. Issues in training the new non-professional, 1967 (unpublished).

Rioch, M., Elkes, C., & Flint, A. A. *Pilot Project in training mental health counselors.* U.S.D.H.E.W., PHS No. 1254, 1965.

Wallace, W. Urban conditions that challenge the university. *Education Research Special Supplement,* Summer, 1965, p. 317.

Weed, V., & Denham, W. H. Toward more effective use of the nonprofessional worker: a recent experiment. *Social Work,* 1961, *6,* (4), 29–36.

Youth Studies Center. *Experiment in culture expansion—Proceedings of the conference on the use of products of a social problem in coping with the problem.* University of Southern California, Youth Studies Center, 1963.

Chapter 11
The Planning Project
for Columbia

Paul V. Lemkau

The outstanding feature of Dr. Lemkau's chapter is the depth of his personal involvement in the planning of a new community. Such involvement not only requires integrated knowledge of mental health principles but the unique ability to work with and communicate to people who are often far outside the health and welfare field. However, it is this ability that is essential if any primary prevention programs in mental health are to be effective.

One gratifying aspect of planning a new community is that it is not necessary to deal with already existing agencies that have established traditions and ways of working. The focus is rather on the political and social forces through which new service organizations can emerge to meet the health and welfare needs that are developing within the young growing community.

Chapter 11

The Planning Project
for Columbia

Paul V. Lemkau

I had put a time on the office calendar to meet with an architect who said he represented a firm that intended to build a new city somewhere near Baltimore and Washington. The city would eventually have a population of something over 100,000 persons. He was unable to tell me where the city was to be exactly because land was still being acquired and the knowledge of the site had to be kept secret.

When we met, the aims of the city were outlined a bit more clearly. The entrepreneur was a stable firm and had the unusual opportunity of being well capitalized. I was told that one trouble with most suburban developments is that they are undercapitalized and are, therefore, usually unable to think in grand terms because from the very start quick sales have to dominate everything. In this case the developer had the capital and was resolved to take the time to plan as carefully as possible what could be done to make the new city what he called "A Garden for People." He told me also that the venture was not a philanthropy, that the developer seriously believed that the capitalist system could produce optimum living conditions at a price which the population could pay, and that the new city could nevertheless yield a profit.

Reston, Virginia, and the California Retirement Village were much in the news about that time, and I was discouraged by the fact that they seemed to be aimed exclusively at housing the middle and upper classes. My ingrained public health attitudes made me suspicious that Columbia—the name had not been settled at that time—would be just another such, with no mix of population at all. I was told, quite frankly, that no organization hoping to make a profit could build housing for people on welfare, but that it was the intent to provide housing within the range of rents or purchase prices of anyone who held a job in the town. Having some liberal leanings, I asked also about racial segregation and was assured that, aside from the economic segregation inevitable then and now, the community would be nonsegregated.

When I demurred in the usual academic fashion on the ground that my time was already full and that the job of consultation loomed very large, my friend the architect-planner got a little rough. He didn't have anything on me in print, but he knew that I and my kind had said some harsh things about urban sprawl, the negative aspects of the fatherless state in commuter villages, the disadvantages of the separation of facilities necessary for living from the place of the home, the poverty of existence of wives in unplanned developments, the deadly sameness of repetitious house design, etc., including a few things about stinking septic tanks that don't work properly and are a threat to health. He said that these sorts of things were what the developer wanted to avoid and, in more polite language, indicated that now was the time to put up or shut up. He did a good job of making me feel that I would be letting my specialty down if I stayed in my ivory tower this time. Reality beckoned.

I was asked to be the consultant for a very large field—health, welfare, and mental health. This, I said, was too much; the response was that opportunity was opened for me to organize a group to cover these areas, with myself to represent the whole at the consultants' meetings. This I agreed to do, and soon I became deeply involved in the process.

The consultants were really consultants, that is, they had no directorial power—the developer was free to accept or reject advice. He and his top staff, however, bound themselves to the same discipline that the consultants did; and they attended every meeting and listened to all the interchange. A person skilled in group dynamics was hired to be the chairman, to see to it that the group did not get mired down, to push toward conclusions when this was possible, and to keep order in the lively discussions. His prodding also served to get written and verbal reports before the group for specific discussion and criticism. Because he believes that this project has importance for the future, the developer soon added a historian to the group to keep a record of what was going on.

The central group of consultants comprised various disciplines chosen to represent the gamut of those concerned in the life of a city, with particular stress on its interpersonal and cultural life. The physical aspects were represented by the skills incorporated in the developing company—people with architectural, engineering, financing, and city planning experience. We were a mixture of academicians and former academicians, and most had field research or practical administrative experience, some specifically in connection with town planning and its results, others in less directly related ventures. Lists are tiresome but seem necessary here. The group included sociologists who were activists or students in community program operation. It included a political scientist and a city manager. There was an educational consultant and a special subgroup that met separately on higher education. There was a library planner, a communications expert, a transportation consultant, a lawyer who doubled as the representative of housewives, and economists, one specializing in economic structure and another specializing in housing and housing market analysis. The religious organization of the new community was discussed in a separate interdenominational group; the central group of consultants did not hear its discussion but only saw its results, which were among the most exciting of all produced.

The Health and Welfare group for which I was the spokesman included a pediatrician-maternal and child health expert, a biometrician, a health insurance expert, a health educator, a health economist, a social work educator, a specialist in chronic diseases, a public health dentist, an obstetrician, a public health administrator, a hospital service analyst, and a medical sociologist, Guido Crocetti, who was vice-chairman and helped in running the group and in writing the report. Again, it must be noted that this group was specifically asked not to deal with the problems of water supply, sanitation, or surface drainage, etc., the province of sanitary engineering. The province of the consultants was the area of human interrelationships and how the physical structure of the community could lead to health in the area of living—health in its broadest definition.

By this time it had become known where Columbia would be located—an area of rolling land interlaced by streams, of about 25 square miles in Howard County, Maryland. The area had a population of about 8,000 people, some on farms and some in developments that would be engulfed by the new city. It lay on a road that was in the process of being converted from a secondary to a dual lane one, and it lay in the path of a completely new expressway connecting Baltimore and Washington.

The first task in approaching the planning problem was to get over the feeling of awe at the size of the proposed new city. It was estimated that it would take 15 years to build the city. One day the discussion got onto the question of power supply, and the group found itself discussing the feasibility of having a nuclear plant for the production of electricity. The rate of building was proposed as 2,500 houses per year. The city we were contemplating was one the size of Racine, Wisconsin, and twice that of Hagerstown, Maryland. The very size of the venture was sobering.

The staff had done a good deal of geographic work. The best stands of forest—and there are some magnificent individual trees as well as forests—had been plotted, and the areas providing views to the community had been exploited or preserved for common use and had been mapped. The streams had been studied as to their usual and unusual flow patterns so that areas safe from flooding were known. The functions of the streams in providing barriers within the area had been looked into, as had their possible function in supplying artificial lakes for recreation. Their steep banks in some areas precluded building economically on them and made them obvious candidates for relatively undeveloped, natural areas not to be lightly interfered with.

Once the size of the venture had been grasped and the awe it inspired (at least in those of us from low-financed academic atmospheres) had been dispelled, the question that hovered over all others came to the fore and remained there. This was, I think, primarily a political-ethical issue. It can be stated quite simply:

"How much ought one to plan the life of another, regardless of the bona fide intentions of the planner?" It was recognized that every time a decision was made, it would affect the life of someone who would one day live in Columbia and would restrict his freedom to some extent, even though the freedom he wished to exercise might be a violation of someone else's freedom. It was the old problem of when the restriction of freedom becomes tyranny, and when freedom merges into license. The question haunted all discussion so much that it had to be made a joke of—when the issue came up we called the entrepreneur the "Baron of Columbia." He, as concerned as everyone else that the "Garden for People" not become a prison for people and that freedom to grow not become growing row on row in strictly channelized patterns, ruefully had to accept the responsibility for the fact, but depended upon the consultants and his own sensitive conscience to maintain the greatest freedom for the future inhabitants while protecting the facilities for the good and free life as well.

This gnawing question appeared in a hundred different guises. Obviously one cannot allow a $15,000 house to abut a $65,000 one; how can the two be positioned so that neither interferes with the life of the other intolerably? This problem was discussed in terms of the research that had been done on the subject, interpreting mostly how people have reacted in the past to mixing property values and the kinds of locations that were tolerable. Parks, mostly along the streams, and recreation areas, mostly about the schools, were planned. When Columbia was completed and the ownership of the public lands transferred to a governmental body, how could they be protected from invasion by rival "goods," say a school or church or industry that boded well for the community economy? Community spirit, a sense of belongingness, minimum risk of anomie were agreed to be suitable ideals for "A Garden for People." Yet there are people who want mostly to be left alone, and their rights required protection too. It would be much easier to finance a sound program of supervised recreation if everyone somehow was required to help pay for it. But could it be said to be proved that such a program was of sufficient worth to all so that all should be obliged to pay for it in an official or unofficial tax pattern? Comprehensive health services were recognized to be a desideratum of very great value, but is it fair—and in this instance economically sound—to impose a tax to provide them, even on those who do not want to get their services in a prescribed way? Of course, it is true that no one can be forced to live in Columbia and that the principle of informed consent could be used when people were considering buying, but could consent really be informed? Preoccupied with multiple problems and the fact that most of them could be solved only relatively, the consultants rather doubted that a prospective buyer could be really informed in advance of all the possible restrictions on his freedom that could be exercised. The patient cannot know everything his surgeon knows when he gives his consent to an operation, yet he should if it is really to be informed consent.

Such questions as those were always before the group. The ideal was set as maintaining the balance in the direction of freedom wherever possible, and planning only those things that had to be planned, leaving for future discussion, in which the then inhabitants of Columbia could participate, everything possible. There were still plenty of decisions to be made.

One of the first encountered was the question of the size of the population group to be considered the unit of the new city. The streams and other topographical features of the land made natural barriers that could, if one wished, be utilized as barriers or separations between population groups. Should they be so used, or should the primary identification be with the eventual hundred thousand population of the city? And if the decision were made that local rather than city-wide identification was to be fostered, then how could the total community, not only Columbia but the county and state, also have a fair share of identification and loyalty?

The consultants agreed that one of the major losses in the process of growth of American cities has been that of local community feeling as the original towns became contiguous, cities grew, and local identification deteriorated. The big city is too disparate and too large, somehow, to evoke a concern for all of it. Pride in a neighborhood and the ability to influence others to maintain a real basis for that pride are very difficult to maintain when the area and number of people become too large. No community appears to have been able to maintain the local feeling of belongingness in large cities at a scale that can be genuinely influential, and to build this feeling after it has become dissipated requires intensive and often expensive effort. Such considerations as these led to the conclusion that Columbia should be laid out in such a way that a more local primary identification would be fostered.

The next question was how large should the local groups be? Several factors entered consideration at this point. One that was primarily more important than we realized at the time was the tendency to idealize the American small town, which, despite *Main Street* and *Peyton Place,* appears still to have its place in our tradition. But more rational factors also entered. The population necessary to support a small shopping center providing the necessary variety of goods to allow comfortable and somewhat exciting everyday shopping is about 10,000 to 15,000 people. About the same number will supply enough pupils for junior high schools of the size that the educational consultant believed to be optimum. The junior high school and shopping center would supply the focal points for a community of 10,000 to 15,000, then; and around these determining institutions could be ranged recreation areas, churches, professional offices, etc. The school could be planned for multiple uses—clubs, programs for special groups such as theatrical clubs, craft clubs, music groups, special program groups for the aged, etc. Local health services could stem from professional buildings constructed in advance in such a manner as to foster group practice without dictating that it should exist. Local public health services, including physicians' services, were conceived of as being housed as an expansion of the necessary school health suites in school buildings, with the local physicians' offices nearby so that part-time and emergency services would be obtainable conveniently. Early in the planning, high schools were to be specialized and serve the entire city. Later both junior and senior high schools became village institutions.

The goal that all students should be able to walk to school was established early, and the conclusion followed that each neighborhood would have several elementary schools of the size considered optimum by the educational consultant. Each school would form a center for a smaller, much less pretentious commercial development, consisting of community rooms, swimming pool, and the "Seven-Eleven" type of store[1] to satisfy emergency needs for food and sundries.

Children walking to school require that traffic safety have a high priority. The encouragement of a friendly community atmosphere that would not be discouraged by traffic barriers was another goal, and the esthetic aspect of the problem of wide glaring roadways covered with brilliantly colored, highly reflecting automobiles was not overlooked. Reduced to physical planning terms, these considerations led to the grade separation of walkways and roadways at crossings and to a local small-bus transportation system traveling on its exclusive roads to connect the 10 or 12 villages envisioned at this point in planning.

As has been stated, there was concern that Columbia as a city should have an identity of its own. Furthermore, a community of 100,000 people generates demands beyond those suggested as being satisfiable at the level of the village of 10,000 to 15,000 people. In practical terms, this means such things as larger items of furniture, appliances, a wider range of selection of kinds of articles such as department stores provide, central banking functions, offices for government officials, specialists in medicine and law, and higher education functions. The less popular but highly valuable cultural and recreational items such as concert halls, museums, exhibits, and also hospital services were items that the larger population would need.

Housing also had to be provided for two special groups of people—those who prefer to live in a downtown area rather than in a suburban setting, and those whose mobility is reduced by reason of disability or advanced age who want to live in a distinctly urban situation because their conditions necessitate it.

All of these considerations dictated a city center of high rise buildings with the hustle and some of the crowding implicit in them, which some people want

---

[1]Seven-Eleven stores are small, usually family-operated establishments dealing in food and notions items that may be needed for minor household emergencies such as unexpected guests. The name comes from the fact that they open at 7:00 a.m. and close at 11:00 p.m. and are thus available when stores with large stocks are closed.

and many people appear to need as a regular item in the American cultural diet.

There was much discussion about whether centralizing these services in a high-rise area would cause it to become the focus of a Columbia-wide identification, or whether some special symbolic structure representing the city should be created to meet this need. An alternative possibility was the planning of some extraordinary place that would lend itself to becoming the identifying symbol. Many things were discussed, the imposing tower capable of being seen from many places with the usual restaurant on top of it à la Rotterdam, Tivoli gardens à la Copenhagen, and a number of other things. I think it can be said that the importance of this objective to the consultants receded the longer it was discussed, with the size and extraordinary character of the object that should stand as the symbol of the total city becoming less specific and a less dominating factor in the consultants' minds. I believe that this represented a kind of realization that the inevitable artificiality of an imposing symbol, designed before the time that the community could have a "self" to express, could never be genuine. And even if a symbol were to be built, perhaps it would be necessary to allow the passage of time in order to see what character the community might develop and wish to symbolize for itself. Eventually the conclusion seemed to have been reached that the cultural, educational, professional, living, economic, and recreational needs would, in the process of being satisfied, provide the symbolic center for Columbia with which all its neighborhoods could identify.

Adult education required much discussion. It was not possible to conceive of Columbia as a self-contained city; indeed, the principal reason for its planning was recognition of the inevitable influx of population to the Baltimore-Washington corridor to satisfy the manpower needs of those two cities. Nevertheless, there was the goal that the new city should be more than a mere satellite or bedroom town; and it was a hope, sustained by the opinion of economists, that the city would furnish employment for about half of its inhabitants, this employment being in light industries to be attracted and in the services that these industries required. Industries were to be principally located so that their traffic would not come through Columbia and so that workers could use the internal bus service already described. The sorts of industries envisioned were likely to be faced with rapidly changing demands that could require relatively well-trained workers and rather frequent retraining of the labor force. One of the aims of the educational structure of the community would be to provide a trainable worker and to furnish facilities adaptable to changing demand for retraining workers when needed. There was, of course, no intent to sacrifice academic or cultural education; rather, the goal was to integrate with these a suitable, flexible vocational training, from workbench to executive office. The entrepreneur of Columbia believed that the ability of the community to provide such an educational program would prove more attractive to industry of the type suitable for its setting than would mere cheapness of location, low taxes, or cheap labor. And, he was willing to bet on his belief. The consultants had much sympathy with the basic concept that it was important for the educational system to be prepared to meet challenges in the field of vocational education as well as academic education and to meet them with flexibility and in creative ways.

*   *   *

Columbia stands in a county which, prior to its advent, had been growing with moderate rapidity but had reached a total population of only 40,000 before the new city threatened to triple its total population. The new city could not be built until rather radical changes were made in the county zoning laws, which were directed mainly toward preserving the open agricultural character of the landscape and, to some extent, toward the encouragement of industry. The area has a strong sense of tradition, sustained by families whose histories there go back to colonial days. Details will not be discussed in this paper, but the process by which the county reached the point of acceptance of the inevitable population explosion and of the wisdom of placing responsibility for the planning for a portion of it in the hands of the developer of Columbia is itself worthy of special study.

The county had a public health department that incorporated in its total services specialty clinics, including a limited mental health program. The welfare department is small and carries a small load in relation to the population of the county. The educational system has built a number of new schools, some of which have been recognizable attempts to stem desegregation by providing separate but equal accommodations for the relatively small Negro population.

It became clear quite early in the planning period that Columbia would be governed within the existing county system. Other methods of government, including the establishment of an incorporated city and the design of a special tax district, were considered but disregarded as impractical or requiring changes in the law that would be very time-consuming, if obtainable at all. From this it would be deduced that for the services it wanted beyond those provided through the county government, Columbia would have to use some sort of voluntary taxing system, but that its basic service structure would have to be that of the county of which it was to be a part.

These considerations were important in the work of the health and welfare consultant group. They meant that whatever other health and welfare services were to be introduced into the new community, the basic level of tax-supported services would be those available to all citizens of the county. There was considerable sentiment in favor of a comprehensive program of prepaid medical and preventive medicine services, and much thought was given to the manner in which this might be accomplished. The particular problem that harassed the group was how the various health plans that the inhabitants would bring with them to Columbia could be integrated into a single plan that could, hopefully, be more comprehensive than any one of them. The medical economist struggled with this question; but because the issues of constructing and managing hospital and outpatient services could not be solved during the planning period, no final recommendations could be made. Subsequently, the Johns Hopkins Hospital has agreed to furnish medical care services and to service the local hospital; yet the financing problems are not entirely solved even after three years.

Much thought was given to the problem of what hospital services should be supplied to the citizens of Columbia. The new city stands between two outstanding medical teaching centers, so it was early concluded that Columbia's hospital should have the character of a satellite or regional institution rather than aim to supply complete services. Thus, heart and neurosurgery and other highly specialized or technical services requiring very elaborate equipment and specially trained personnel should not be included. The distance to the existing complete medical centers (approximately twenty miles) could be covered safely by ambulance, either automobile or helicopter.

What services, then, should be provided locally? The first is shortstay emergency service. Columbia is located amid a complex of major highways, so traumatic surgery needs heavy representation. Predictions are that the incoming population will be rather young, so obstetric and maternal and child care services need to be somewhat larger proportionately than for a mature community. There was much discussion about the need for inpatient pediatric care; the consultants reached the conclusion that in the light of the latest experience in this field, it perhaps was not needed. Acute problems are usually treated at home, and most pediatric inpatient care requires very elaborate laboratory services and frequently long hospital stay, which can be done best in a few highly specialized, complete centers. Children's surgery, except for trauma, is so rarely an emergency that the distance to major pediatric service did not dictate the creation of specialized services locally. On the other hand, the newer ideals of psychiatric services demand a sound service in the local hospital. Not all the population would be young; this consideration implies the need for an emergency and therapeutic service to deal with cardiovascular catastrophes. These principles, general and otherwise, were reduced to numbers; and recommendations were made as to the size of hospital and distribution of beds according to the envisioned needs. It was recommended that the hospital building be so constructed that the size of the various services could be flexible, in order to meet unforeseen needs and unpredictable changes in medical practice.

Home care and office care services could not be thoroughly planned, either, since it was not known whether they would be supplied by entrepreneurial practitioners or under a prepaid plan of some sort. In the face of these unknowns, it was recommended first that physician office buildings be built in the village centers and that efforts be made to discourage practice from other points in the town; physicians entering Columbia should not be allowed to build home-offices. The village medical buildings should be so constructed that solo practice would be discouraged while the grouping of physicians would be encouraged. Thus, as a starting point toward this objective, waiting rooms serving several physicians were recommended; and it was proposed that provision be made for clinical laboratories to be shared.

The problem of recording data on the health and social condition of the population was carefully considered. Discussions on this point were dominated by the hovering feeling that much about Columbia represents a social experiment and that as such it should be carefully and scientifically observed so that lessons learned here would not be lost. One idea that kept recurring was that there should exist a comprehensive data bank into which the factors of health and social adjustments of all sorts might be fed, from library card holding to coronary heart disease. The statisticians of the health and welfare group recommended finally that this not be attempted. One reason was their conviction that the massing of data prior to clear formulation of the questions they were to help answer was wasteful and, on the basis of experience, usually proved to not contain the data needed when a clear question was asked. The second reason was more general and dealt with the ethical problem of freedom from restrictive surveillance, discussed earlier in this paper. Anterospective data were recognized as having many advantages over retrospectively collected material; but unless one knows clearly what one wants to find out, one cannot know what data to collect anterospectively. The conclusion was, then, that the data that each functioning unit of Columbia needs for its own operations and planning would be collected, but that the objective of combining all in a single data bank would prove too expensive in money, in personal restrictions, and in the invasion of privacy and would not be justified by any prospect of clear and valuable research purposes.

Welfare planning was not very detailed. Of course, it was recommended that "mortgage insurance" schemes be incorporated in financing homes so that housing emergencies because of death or prolonged disability would be minimized. These plans are suggested by private insurance companies as a relatively standard procedure, and the idea appeared to give little concern to the economist-financiers. They were considered important by the mental hygiene representative as a means of reducing stresses on families. It was recognized that death and disability, as well as other contingencies would begin to produce a welfare load in the new city very early. The need to provide for the county-wide welfare system to operate in Columbia was recognized, not only for the relief of poverty but in its other functions of child protection and placement, old age assistance, etc. A particularly difficult problem was to predict how much help the basic tax-supported system might need from voluntary agencies. Would a family and children's agency evolve, or has the fading tradition of voluntarism reached a point at which a new community cannot be expected to continue the tradition? Obviously this question could only be recorded as an area to be carefully watched, so that action could be initiated as need and opportunity might arise, depending upon the presence of appreciated need and the simultaneous emergence of citizen leadership. Another particularly troublesome question was how to manage the housing of welfare recipients. It has been pointed out that new housing cannot be paid for at welfare rates, yet it seemed inconceivable that the brave, new, complete city of which the consultants dreamed could exclude everyone who might require public assistance. If it did, could it be called complete?

The goals of "The Garden for People" and of promoting mental health and preventing the mental illnesses of nonspecific etiology are so nearly alike that there was little to be initiated by the specialist in mental health. Parent education in child development was included in the nursery school program proposals, in the adult education planning, and as an integral part of maternal and child care. Educational counseling, backed up when necessary by psychiatric consultation and services, was inseparable from educational planning. Crisis information will be provided through the availability of local public health nursing personnel who are to work closely with the medical practitioners. This will be facilitated by placing the physicians' office buildings near the schools, which are to include the local health department representatives.

Particular effort is to be exercised to maintain continuous prenatal care for the protection of the central nervous system, among other things. Thought was given to the problems of adolescents, with resultant attention to recreational opportunities for them. In addition, much thought was given to making part-time employment available to adolescents, in ways such as manning busses or working as salespeople during peak load hours, which would not interfere with school hours. It was thought that school buildings might be made adaptable to other community needs to be so used in the event that proves desirable. Volunteer and part-time services to meet some community needs are to be developed for housewives. There was discussion as to whether all such services should perhaps be paid, in order to discourage the formation of highly noticeable social distinctions between those who work for money and those whose work is charitable. All these questions and more were matters of serious concern to most members of the consultant group; it was a place where a mental hygienist could not be lonely.

A special responsibility did rest upon him as an objective scientist, however. This was to warn that none of all the proposed prophylactic measures could be expected to be entirely successful. Mentally retarded and otherwise handicapped children not only would arrive with their families in Columbia, but would be born there. They must be provided for, hopefully not in as large a proportion of the population as elsewhere, because of factors such as selective population and healthful environment, but they will exist. Elderly persons will come with the younger ones; and while a healthful environment and good medical care may delay their deterioration, eventually some of them will become senile and require special care. There is little to indicate that a healthful environment affects the rate of occurrence of schizophrenia whatsoever, and the incoming population will be largely in the age group where there is high risk of this disease. Depressions may be even more common than in an unselected population, both because depressions seem to occur more frequently in people who bear responsibility well and because of the grief reactions associated with losing old friends as well as the stress reactions of making new friends and adaptations. Injecting these chilling notions often became necessary when the consultants' enthusiasm became so great that a necessary community service seemed to be in danger of being underplanned.

*   *   *

The character of this year-long consultation venture was quite different from the author's previous experience, which had been mainly in educational and administrative consultation where an academic approach is appropriate. It is no accident that no bibliography is included with this paper; where would one start, and how would he ever stop, when he tried to think of all the aspects of the life of the individual and the family in the community? At every point in composing such a report one may consult literature, but usually each point is so infinitesimal in relation to the whole that it seems ludicrous to insist upon documenting it.

It seemed to me that the other consultants in the group had reached the conclusion that I had reached quite early—namely, that the pressure for action was so great that one could depend only on a judgment that he had formed through an assimilation, sometimes conscious but often unconscious, of myriad items of data gleaned through study and field experience, a judgment of which he was very confident. There was no time to marshal documentation, and it would have been meaningless to a large degree outside of one's own specialty in any event. The result was that one sat as an expert and hoped that he was. He had the comfortable feeling that others in the group spoke from the same type of background, and usually he felt entirely secure in granting this expertise. Of course, this is a familiar situation to the administrator, but there is a difference, too. The true consultant can anticipate looking up things later at his leisure and having his books at hand when he writes his report. The administrator, however, often finds himself catapulted from one problem to another at such a rate that he never has the leisure to check back on himself. To the extent that this is true, it places a heavier burden on the administrator.

Final Words

There has been substantial interest in recent years in new ideas, new approaches, and new resources in the prevention, treatment, and rehabilitation of mental illness and related psychosocial problems. These new efforts differ from those of earlier years in several ways:

1. Explanations of problems have broadened beyond that of seeking deficiencies within the individual personality, to that of looking as well at the total social and cultural context as related to behavior disturbances.

2. Interventions are often directed at large populations or groups rather than the individual.

3. New techniques of intervention, such as consultation, collaboration, mental health education, and community organization, have become standard in the armamentarium of the mental health practitioner; treatment strategies have tended to become more crisis oriented and short term and are directed at family and extended family groups.

4. New personnel are being trained to work with the traditional mental health disciplines as child development specialists, human service aides, and mental health facilitators.

All of this strongly implies a rather radical shift in departure on all fronts—intervention strategies, training, administration, and program evaluation. The papers in this volume are illustrative of innovations in the areas listed above. They are essentially mental health approaches to community problems, directed and staffed by mental health professionals and those in allied disciplines. A number of them are based in familiar mental health settings, such as an outpatient center or a general hospital; others are in new settings, such as stores or business offices. Brought together, they serve the purpose of demonstrating how specific programs have been designed to meet the needs that have arisen out of community problems. They are not intended to serve as a manual. If the authors have elicited discussion and/or controversy out of which new programs, new ideas, or new strategies will be generated, the volume will have served its purpose.

Index